Black Swan Ghosts

A sociologist encounters witnesses to unexplained aerial craft, their occupants, and other elements of the multiverse

Simeon Hein, PhD

Black Swan Ghosts

A sociologist encounters witnesses to unexplained aerial craft, their occupants, and other elements of the multiverse

Simeon Hein, PhD

ISBN 978-0-9715863-2-1

Black Swan Ghosts: A sociologist encounters witnesses to unexplained aerial craft, strange beings, and other elements of the multiverse.

by Simeon Hein, PhD

©2017 Mount Baldy Press, Inc. Boulder, Colorado

www.MountBaldy.com orders@mountbaldy.com tel: 415-413-8052

This book is dedicated to Colin Andrews, Steven Bassett, Dr. John O'Meara Bockris, Dr. Courtney Brown, Lyn Buchanan, Dr. Steven Greer, Dr. Ed May, Joe McMoneagle, Dr. Hal Puthoff, Ron Russell, Ingo Swann, Russell Targ, and many other brave pioneers for their tireless dedication in pursuit of the truth about the strange universe in which we live. And to the courage of the many witnesses herein to come forward and tell us their stories. Without them and their dogged persistence and integrity, our understanding of the universe in which we live would be much less complete. And thanks to Pam Bealer for text editing, style suggestions, and general encouragement.

Contents

Preface

This is a book I never thought I'd write. It's a topic that, for me, really came out of nowhere and seems to keep growing on its own. It's not something I was looking for but seems to have found me. After getting to know many credible first or second-hand witnesses over the last twenty years, to what appear to be unidentifiable craft and beings, reviewing all the available evidence, and attending countless conferences and related events, I felt compelled to present this material. Clearly and without a doubt, something unexplained is going on in our skies and on the ground.

At one point in my life, this topic seemed like something you'd be interested in as a teenager and then grow out of as you grew up and became wiser. Not anymore.

It's important for me to mention that I didn't seek out any of the witnesses in this book: they're nearly all people who wanted to tell me their stories for lack of anyone to talk to who would take them seriously. It's not their fault that they've witnessed something for which our society has no explanation. But this isn't reason enough to leave them in an emotional and psychological limbo at best. Rather than run away from this mystery, and seek to discredit otherwise credible witnesses, we should be asking hard questions about what it all means. What exactly are they experiencing?

And let me point out that the witnesses you'll hear from in the following pages are just the proverbial tip of the iceberg. These just happen to be people I know very well or spent a lot of time with. And I'm just one person who wasn't even particularly looking for this information. How many others are there with similar experiences who remain silent? You probably know some yourself and aren't even aware of it.

We're fortunate that some of the witnesses here granted me extensive, detailed, and astounding live interviews. You can find these interviews on the Black Swan Ghosts website. When I've put the video interview or additional material online, you'll see a notification at the end of the chapter, like this: *[Video available for this chapter]*. Just go to the website link **BlackSwanGhosts.com/videos**[1] and you'll see the video interview links.

Topics like this eventually need to be addressed, or I'm convinced the people who've experienced this type of phenomena will end up with unnecessary psychological harm as will our entire national psyche. But let me explain to you first how I got involved.

---

[1] http://blackswanghosts.com/videos

Introduction

We must be bold and go hunting for the truth; even if we do not come right up to it, at least we will get closer to it than we are now.—Galen

In 1996, while listening to my local community radio station, I heard about something called "remote viewing," purportedly the ability of a person to perceive non-local information about distant places, people, and events. Also known as "anomalous cognition" and other names, because there is no obvious explanation for how it worked, the U.S. military and intelligence agencies funded what turned out to be a twenty-year project to develop this faculty for intelligence gathering purposes. Several cadres of psychic spies were trained to do remote viewing and use it for operational purposes for many government agencies. This Special Access Program, or SAP as they're known, was declassified in 1995.

As they are known, the "remote viewers" did work for numerous government law enforcement and intelligence agencies for years. One of them, Joe Mc-Moneagle, was even given a Legion of Merit award, the highest peacetime award bestowed by the military, for over 200 remote viewing sessions that the government asserted had yielded over 150 pieces of valuable intelligence information (Ed May, *ESP Wars: East and West*). And he was only one of several highly accurate viewers employed by the government. Some of the other original viewers in the program, such as Ingo Swann and Pat Price, did equally accurate work so that it completely astonished the intelligence community.

At the 2013 International Remote Viewing Conference, Christopher "Kit" Green, a retired high-ranking official in the Central Intelligence Agency who backed the remote viewing program, described how three remote viewing sessions, done for him as tests, completely surprised him in their accuracy and precision. One of these sessions involved the National Security Agency facility in Sugar Grove, West Virginia, where the two viewers at Stanford Research Institute, thousands of miles away, were able to not only describe the building structures in great detail but also successfully identify and name classified project codenames that were physically locked in a secured safe.

Although I doubted that ordinary people had such a skill, I decided to enroll in a week-long class in remote viewing in 1996, taught by Dr. Courtney Brown, a political science professor at Emory University. To my surprise and shock, it seemed like everyone in the class, including myself, got positive results in just a few days. Students seemed to be able to describe pictures of events and locations that wouldn't be shown to them until they had written down all their perceptions. This completely upended my sense of reality and disturbed my idea of what type of universe we inhabit. I wasn't prepared for remote viewing to work *that well.* My graduate training in sociology hadn't prepared me for such a phenomenon to be real. At best, the sociological theory I had learned would have described it as an "urban legend" or "why do people believe in weird things." But here it was in front of me, quite real and undeniable.

It seemed clear that the average person could accurately describe a picture of their viewing "target" or objective that they wouldn't physically see until a few minutes, hours, or days later. This event is known in RV parlance as their "feedback." Independent statistical analysis by Jessica Utts, as of this writing head of the American Statistical Association, for the special Congressional review board, concluded that remote viewing was real. Participants got about 8 percent more information correct than they would if they guessed, and at a very high statistical significance or confidence level.

Utts summarized: "Using the standards applied to any other area of science, you have to conclude that certain psychic phenomena, such as remote viewing, have been well established. The results are not due to chance or flaws in the experiments."

Subsequent work by Dean Radin (author of *En-*

tangled Minds, *The Conscious Universe, Supernormal* and other instructive, comprehensive books on the subject) and others have shown similar conclusions.

Social danger zones

Learning about natural human psychic perception led me to have curiosity about other related topics like UFOs, the possibility of ET life, crop circles, and life after death. I wrote about some of these subjects in my first book *Opening Minds: A Journey of Extraordinary Encounters, Crop Circles, and Resonance* in 2002. Those topics continue to challenge me, even today, as they do many other researchers.

At the time of publishing *Opening Minds*, I assumed the general public and the media would be interested in new science topics like these. And the response has been terrific. But I've also encountered another countervailing phenomenon to opening minds: staying stuck in older beliefs despite massive evidence to the contrary. And even worse, an unwillingness to look at the evidence or to look the other way.

It's not just that people don't want to look at new evidence for "hard to believe" phenomena. I think it's much more than that.

Beginning with my experience at Farsight Institute, I've been approached by people who want to

tell me their unusual stories and experiences, often
encounters with unidentifiable aerial vehicles and
their mysterious occupants. Yes, that's what I said,
the *occupants* of these vehicles. And they often are
highly credible people, some with security clearances,
in whom we typically place a lot of responsibility:
astronauts, intelligence officers, and pilots. Some of
them have worked for NASA, the Defense Intelligence
Agency, the U.S. Air Force, defense contractors, various branches of the military, and ordinary people too,
who've just seen something they can't explain.

It's important to note that I haven't sought any of
these witnesses; they all initiated contact with me or
are people I've known for some time.

And for me, they all have one thing in common:
they have no one to talk to about their experiences
of witnessing something different, something that
doesn't easily fit into an idea of reality that we share. If
they disclose this information openly, they feel subject
to ridicule and disparagement. They've gone silent
either because of security clearances or fear or just
being afraid of seeming weird to their colleagues. And
yet, many are highly trained, credible people who've
told me of their experiences that defy anything you or
I were ever taught to believe was real. And they seem
willing to talk to anyone who will listen.

The question is: why don't people feel comfortable
talking about this subject? Why don't they want to

listen? Why the immediate ridicule by our media of these witnesses? In short, why is this topic so threatening to our status quo?

I once heard former newspaper journalist and author Jim Marrs refer to our reaction of disbelief to challenging and hard-to-understand topics as our mental "boggle point." Once you reach the boggle point, it's hard to go any further because your mind is like a rubber band: it snaps back to more familiar, socially acceptable, and comfortable beliefs.

And so might be your reaction to the stories in this book.

Most of the following witness accounts were un-solicited and came about naturally in conversation. In some cases, I'd known these people for many years before they told me these tales, almost like they had to trust me enough before they opened up.

And some cases are not included in the book because the witness felt that their encounter is still so sensitive that there might be personal or national security repercussions if they were mentioned here. Perhaps I'll be able to include these astounding stories in a sequel.

Whether you want to call them UFOs, UAPs (Uniden-tified Aerial Phenomena) as presidential candidate Hillary Clinton started to do, OWCs (off-world craft), AVC (alien visitation craft), or ARVs (alien reproduc-tion vehicles) doesn't matter: some seemingly select group of people on our planet are having interactions with something that is beyond imagination. I'll share some of their stories on the pages below. But the main point is that we don't even have the vocabulary to describe what some of these people have experienced in many cases. And it's beyond weird. And yet, it shows up on radar, often has multiple witnesses, leaves trace marks in the soil, and can sometimes leave short and long-term physiological effects on the witnesses. What are we collectively dealing with?

I honestly never imagined as a younger person that the universe we live in contained such immediate and direct strangeness. It was one thing to watch Carl Sagan on TV tell us about our universe's sheer magnitude and scope: but he never mentioned anything like this.

And I also never imagined that the society we live in is so compartmentalized, squelched, and silenced that there's virtually no serious discussion about this critical topic. The mainstream media just completely ignores it.

Whether you think extraterrestrials, interdimensionals, or fairy spirits are visiting us doesn't matter. It's that individuals and groups, highly trained professionals in some cases, are having experiences that are incredibly strange yet cannot be officially discussed. Why?

I think about this subject area as a *Social Danger*

Zone: because it's scary to talk about and even more frightening, in the long run, not to talk about. Either way, from the point of view of our current social milieu, you lose. Some, like political lobbyist Stephen Bassett, organizer of the Citizen Hearing on Disclosure held at the National Press Club in Washington, D.C., in 2013, say it's like you've touched the electrified third rail on a train track: your career will just end. So people who've witnessed this type of thing have nowhere to go, no one to find support from, and a society ready to ridicule, denigrate and harass them at the very least. When you open up about this stuff, you risk everything.

Is this a case of mass delusion? Not on the part of the witnesses but by society for refusing to deal with large groups of people who've said they've seen something they can't describe?

We're told that we have a free press and media. But where are they on this issue? Hillary Clinton was the Democratic Party's candidate and the clear winner of the popular vote in the 2016 presidential election. Her chief advisor, John Podesta, also a former advisor to presidents Clinton and Obama, *explicitly asked the press to query her about the topic of UFOs.* He hinted that she knew something more about the subject. (She did discuss it with Laurence Rockefeller in 1993-96 as part of a hidden presidential effort now known as the "Rockefeller Initiative"). Yet, for the most part, the media won't discuss it. Is it because they've been told not to, by something or someone, or is there a deeper reason? Are we all afraid to find out that the universe we live in isn't what we thought it was? Do we tacitly want the press to remain silent and blame some "secret government" instead?

Flatland

In 1882, Edwin A. Abbott wrote a book called *Flatland: An adventure in many dimensions,* a parody of Victorian England and its quirks. The book is a fictional piece about the world of two-dimensional creatures who live on a flat surface and don't believe in any higher dimensions. Hence, there is no such thing as a 3-D object to them. One day, one of them, "A Square," encounters a sphere moving through Flatland. It talks to him and tells him about the 3rd dimension, "Spaceland." Surprised and incredulous, A Square tells other people about his experience. He is subsequently arrested, tried, and imprisoned for talking about his experience with the sphere. And at the end of the book, we find that the leaders of Flatland have known about Sphereland all along but were afraid of the social repercussions if the denizens of Flatland discovered the truth.

Are our leaders today all that different from Flat-

12

land's who knew the truth but preferred to hide it?

In the following pages, I'll look into the roots of what we're afraid to talk about and why it's so important that we start the discussion now. The longer we wait, the more the risk that we end up in a Social Danger Zone: living in a reality that we don't even have the vocabulary to discuss and can't even talk about. And worse, because we've never talked about it, we could all end up in collective shock where we don't even know where in the universe we are anymore. It would be a sudden cultural dislocation of monumental proportions.

It would take a lot to cause this type of shock. Cortez and his group of fewer than one thousand men were able to conquer millions of people in Central Mexico partly because they thought he was the returning god Quetzequatl and ran away in terror from him. So a lack of knowledge and misinterpretation of evidence can be fatal in the long run. Are we that different than the Central Mexicans of that time?

All of the witness stories contained here were unsolicited by me. None of them were doing it for publicity; they had no books or films to sell. I only heard from these witnesses directly, in some cases many years after I had known them. So I trust all the witnesses in this book because, for the most part, I've known all of them for a long time, and they permitted me to share their experiences with you.

Chapter One—The Robertson Panel

Only puny secrets need keeping. The biggest secrets are kept by public incredulity. —Marshall McLuhan

In 1953, the Central Intelligence Agency appointed a review board, now known as the Robertson Panel, to review evidence from the U.S. Air Force about the large numbers of flying discs that had been seen by the military and the public since the late 1940's. The Panel looked at all the Air Force data, which was itself somewhat biased towards diminishing the phenomena. It concluded that while as much as 20 percent of the cases were unexplained and perhaps unexplainable, the threat of mass panic justified a psychological warfare campaign to dissuade the public from being interested in the phenomenon. The Panel suspected that the Soviet Union could use the situation to its advantage to destabilize the United States.

There had been a plethora of sightings beginning in the late 1940's with sightings of pilot Kenneth Arnold over Mt. Rainer. Then there was the Roswell incident of 1947 with the military itself initially saying it had recovered a flying disc and taken it to Roswell Army Air Field. Sightings in the early 1950's culminated in anomalous objects being repeatedly seen over the nation's Capital in the summer of 1952. The public was baffled, alarmed, and curious about all of it.

And an examination of internal documents shows the U.S. Government's intelligence agencies, the FBI and CIA, and the Air Force weren't sure what to make of it all.

The Air Force conducted its internal studies with contradictory conclusions. The first was known as Project Sign with engineers and scientists at the Foreign Technology Division at Wright-Patterson issuing, and individually signing off on, what was called the "Estimate of the Situation." They concluded these phenomena could be extraterrestrial in origin. There was simply no other explanation that made sense.

However, top Air Force brass like General Vandenberg would not accept such an idea and ordered the Air Force find other explanations for such enigmatic phenomena. So another project was launched in 1949, Project Grudge, to explain away as many UFOs as possible as having more terrestrial explanations.

Sightings continued into the 1950's, especially around nuclear research and energy facilities, especially nuclear power plants. These were solid sightings often with corroboration by Air Force pilots sent to chase these objects away. Though they were named "Green Fireballs" they took a variety of shapes.

A favorite official explanation at the time was

that these objects were a new type Soviet missile that could return to its launch base! Unfortunately, apart from the lack of utility ever suggested for such a technology, *no evidence was ever found to support such a conclusion.* Within the upper echelons of the U.S. Government, there was concern about mass panic and social instability. So programs were created to ridicule the whole subject and dissuade the public from being interested in the first place. Experts, like retired Colonel Richard French, allegedly of Project Blue Book, were instructed to tell individual phone callers that what they had seen was "swamp gas."

At the Citizen Hearing for Disclosure in 2013, French apologized to us but said he was instructed to tell every caller to Blue Book that what they had seen was swamp gas. In every case, no matter what the evidence. In fact, the swamp gas idea was an impromptu explanation that another Blue Book science advisor, J. Allen Hynek, came up with during a press conference about a case in Dexter, Michigan. Hynek said he simply could not think of any other explanation at the time for the strange lights that witnesses saw and later regretted he ever said it. Alternative debunking strategies included saying the witnesses had seen the planet Venus or flocks of birds, no matter how laughable such explanations seemed.

And this program of discrediting witness testimony has continued to this day although now it's done by the media also. After decades of such behavior towards witnesses, no matter how well-qualified and no matter how much corroborating testimony exists, including air and ground radar data, the average person doesn't even know how to talk or think about this subject with any degree of accuracy. The baby has been thrown out with the bathwater. And, at least seventy years ago, that was the intention. There was a fear among our nation's military and intelligence community that such a phenomena could be used by the Soviets, even if they had nothing to do with it directly, to create mass panic during a military conflict.

But to live with this degree of suppression of information, after the Cold War has ended and major hostilities have ceased, no longer seems acceptable. It's not acceptable because we supposedly live in a Democratic Republic: a form of government that can only survive with a free and open discussion of the issues at hand. And the same goes for the media. If we have one area of discourse shuttered and abandoned, then this affects every other area of society and politics. And we end up with a system based mainly on secrecy rather than openness. And democracies and secrecy don't go together very well in the long run.

Similarly, the entire basis of modern science is openness and transparency: especially to open and free discussion of evidence. Without that, science ceases to exist.

Later on, the Condon Committee from 1966 to 1968 was assembled at the University of Colorado in Boulder to ostensibly do a review of all the evidence from the Air Force's Project Blue Book and also sightings from the national organizations NICAP and APRO. Readers can look into this for themselves, but the central figure in this effort was physicist Edward Condon: a former director of the National Bureau of Standards and victim of the McCarthy era for his interest in quantum mechanics. Condon admitted from the beginning that he was biased against the UFO subject and never had a security clearance to view the most sensitive information. The Committee attempted to explain away almost all of the unexplained Blue Book sightings with the common hackneyed explanations including weather balloons, swamp gas, etc. Due to a lack of security clearances, they were completely unaware of the recent UFO sightings over Malmstrom Air Force Base. Malmstrom was home to ICBMs that were taken offline several times by UFOs in 1967, as revealed in an official report by Boeing: events that also occurred many times throughout the United States along the so-called "Northern Tier" SAC bases, and later, other countries as well.

Let me repeat that: the people behind the most complete assessment of the subject, to the present, were not allowed to look at the most serious evidence, namely unexplained aerial phenomena over U.S. nuclear missile sites. Starting in 1967 at Malmstrom base in Great Falls, Montana, entire flights of ICBM missiles were repeatedly shut down, first at Echo Flight, and then at Oscar Flight by unexplained aerial objects that defy explanation to this day. Similar incursions were later reported in the 1960's and 70's at Minot, North Dakota; Ellsworth, South Dakota; Cheyenne, Wyoming; Loring Air Base in Maine; Wurtsmith in Michigan; and others. Since these incursions, including the ones at Malmstrom, were officially marked "classified" they were never part of any civilian UFO investigation. These all had multiple military and civilian witnesses as well as radar data that corroborated the sightings.

Readers can find out more with Robert Hastings book *UFOs and Nukes: Extraordinary Encounters and Nuclear Weapons Sites*, and recent video "UFOs and Nukes: The Secret Link Revealed." Also the books of Robert Salas, *Faded Giant* and *Unidentified: The UFO Phenomenon*, who worked as a missile launch control officer at Malmstrom in the 1960's when these incidents happened. Also, the book *The FBI-CIA-UFO Connection: Government UFO Secrets Revealed at Last!*, by former Naval scientist Bruce Maccabee.

A brief one-day Congressional Hearing on the subject featuring several witnesses, including Stanton

Friedman, in 1968 was the last official government involvement in the issue.

Yet in 1969, General Carol Bolender issued a memo stating that unexplained sightings that could affect national security had been never part of the Blue Book system and instead were reported to what is known as JANAP-146 and Air Force Manual 55-11. The CIRVIS system, as we'll see below, was one such avenue for these type of communications as was another called OPREP-3. None of these files have ever been released according to researcher Stanton Friedman (2016) or Australian investigator Paul Dean.

More significantly, in a telephone conversation ten years later, Bolender admitted to Friedman that UFO cases that affected national security continued to be investigated after Blue Book closed without the public being aware of it.

So throughout the decades since the '50's, the publicly known cases were ridiculed and the really good stuff was, and still is, classified out of public view!

If this subject continues to be belittled, distorted, and ignored, eventually those qualities will come to manifest in every other area of the body politic, society, and the economy. The whole society gets dumbed down, not just in this subject but in our ability to think as a whole about any challenging subject.

Chapter Two—The Citizen Hearing: "Embedded in a shell of silence"

This is the best material I've ever heard . . . but I can't get them to send anyone down from New York to cover it!
— exasperated *New York Times* photographer at the Citizen Hearing

Now let's fast forward to the Spring of 2013. The Citizen Hearing, organized by Steve Bassett of the Paradigm Research Group, was an event held in late April 2013 at the National Press Club in Washington, D.C. It was the most organized and comprehensive look at this phenomena in recent times, if not in history.

Its only predecessor was the Disclosure Project's one-day event at the same National Press Club in May 2001, where thirty witnesses each briefly described their experiences or knowledge of the ET phenomenon before a packed room full of members of the press.

The Citizen Hearing attempted to go beyond the Disclosure Project by having mock hearings for a full five days. Held at the National Press Club just two blocks from the White House, it was perhaps the perfect rebuttal to the Robertson Panel, Project Blue Book, and the Condon Report. I found many of the witnesses to be highly credible and unimpeachable with ground and air radar data confirming many of their sightings.

It included forty witnesses testifying under oath for five days in front of five retired members of Congress and one retired Senator and former presidential candidate, Mike Gravel. Witnesses included retired military pilots, a former FAA official, a former Defense Minister of Canada, astronaut Dr. Edgar Mitchell, and many UFO researchers. All testified to the reality of the phenomena.

Lots of the testimony was riveting, including that of Colonel Oscar Santa Maria of Peru, who described being ordered to shoot down an unidentified object seen by thousands of soldiers on the ground over a Peruvian military base during an exercise. After a frustrating game of cat and mouse, the UFO evaded his fighter plane, even after absorbing twenty-four thirty millimeter cannon rounds from his plane, "each round large enough to destroy a truck" Santa Maria told us.

Rendlesham Forest witness suffers injury from exposure to obsidian colored, triangular craft

Equally fascinating was the testimony of Sergeants Penniston and Burroughs who were at the RAF Bentwaters base in England in 1980 when an unknown object landed in the middle of the night just outside the East gate of the base during Christmas in what came known as the Rendlesham Forest Incident. In this case, over thirty witnesses at Bentwaters which housed Europe's largest storage facility for nuclear weapons witnessed strange, lit objects that were seen over the area, and on the ground for three consecutive nights.

New testimony from another Military Policeman on duty that night, Steve Longero, who said a green and red glowing object moving over the trees looked "like an eye that was almost following everybody," supports that of Penniston and Burroughs who were the first to arrive on the scene on the first night. They later encountered an obsidian black triangular-shaped object inscribed with what looked like hieroglyphics on the forest floor. Burroughs went up and touched the object and suffered eye damage and other internal injuries as a consequence of the electro-magnetic radiation coming from the object. As a result of his testimony, the Dept. of Veteran Affairs agreed to finally give him medical treatment even though the event was still classified, and so were his military health records. Readers interested in this famous case will find more information in *Left at East Gate: A First-Hand Account of the Bentwaters/Woodbridge UFO Incident, Its Cover-up and Investigation*, by Larry Warren and Peter Robbins.

Then there was Dr. Bob Wood, a career employee of forty years of McDonell Douglass, testified to that company's attempts to reproduce UFO technology and propulsion systems. Half a million dollars was invested in the project. They weren't able to do it despite years of research.

I especially enjoyed the testimony from, and my subsequent conversation, with Geoffrey Torres, the son of former Air Force pilot Milton John Torres who was ordered to take off in his F-86D jet and shoot down a huge object in East Anglia, UK in 1957. Torres said the object, which had the "proportions of a flying aircraft carrier" moved at speeds near Mach 10 as it sped up and made right angle turns to avoid his weapons lock. (Torres never saw the object but estimated its size based on its enormous radar return similar to that of a B-52.) According to Torres: *"This thing had to be going double-digit mach making turns that I didn't think were possible, breaking all the rules of physics."* The next day Torres was then visited by a man dressed in a dark blue trench coat from London, showing him credentials of the NSA, who asked him questions about the UFO. He then told Torres that the incident was highly classified and never to mention it again to anyone, not even his commanding officer. Torres would be subject to a security breach if he ever talked about it. Torres complied and never mentioned anything about the event for many years.

Japan Airlines flight 1628 encounters walnut-shaped object the size of an aircraft carrier

John Callahan, formerly a high-ranking official in the FAA and chief of the Accidents and Investigations Division told us the stunning story of the Japan Airlines Flight 1628 that happened in November 1986. As this flight was flying over Alaska, carrying a cargo of wine from Paris to Tokyo, it encountered two large aerial objects, and then a third the size of an aircraft carrier that was shaped like a walnut. All of this was caught on FAA radar from the airport at Anchorage.

The objects were so close the pilot, Captain Terauchi, a former fighter pilot with extensive experience, said he could feel their heat through his cockpit window. And one point the objects stacked themselves vertically, on top of one another, as they flew alongside the 747. They then resumed a side-by-side formation.

Terauchi was told by FAA flight controllers to fly in a complete 360- degree circle to see if the objects followed him and then to land in Anchorage. When Terauchi and his cargo finally made it to Tokyo, he held a press conference and was subsequently assigned by JAL to a desk job as punishment for his openness to talk about the incident.

Callahan told us that Ronald Reagan's science advisors convened a secret meeting with the FBI and CIA to discuss the event back in Washington, D.C. Callahan was ordered to bring the radar tapes but instead surreptitiously brought along copies of the originals. Callahan said to us that after all the events were discussed, CIA officials pointed at everyone and said: **"We're confiscating all the radar data, we were never here, and you're all sworn to secrecy."**

I went up to Callahan after his testimony to the Citizen Hearing and talked to him. He told me privately that the CIA officials said the following: **"We're interested in the radar tapes because we've never had a UFO sighting on tape for this long, usually it lasts just a few minutes."**

Skeptics have provided many alternative explanations for the JAL flight 1628 encounter, such as the planet Venus and temperature inversions. However, recently I met someone, "Joe," who works in a business that supplies the oil industry with technology. He told me he was working on a site in Northern Alaska when he came across an oil worker who had been in the Air Force, stationed in Alaska when the JAL Flight 1628 incident took place. He worked in the radar control room of an Air Force base in Northern Alaska and remembered the incident well. He told Joe that the entire radar room watched the events unfold just as pilot Terauchi described. He said that if the 747 were the size of a very short piece of pencil lead on the radar screen, the largest anomalous craft would have been the size of a quarter, completely engulfing the radar signature of the plane. It was that big! So much for the skeptics' "temperature inversions" and Venus debunking efforts!

Unexplained glowing aerial objects disable ICBMs

I found the four former missile control launch officers for the Strategic Air Command to be some of the most interesting and gripping testimony. They talked about tampering by UFOs with the U.S. strategic ICBMs.

In some cases, at Malmstrom AFB in Montana, the guidance systems were affected such that missiles were no longer online.

One of these launch control officers, Captain David D. Schindele, retired, (pronounced Shin-Delle) was one of the most compelling witnesses at the Citizen Hearing. He served at Minot Air Force Base, in North Dakota, where he had a compelling and unexplained UFO experience in 1966. Schindele had never spoken about this incident in public before, not even to his wife.

He described having seen some reports on the TV news one morning about UFOs being seen in the area the night before. Several hours later he arrived at the base for launch control duty only to find the base in chaos. The night before, as was described to him, an 80-100 foot wide luminous disc had hovered about 100 feet over the base by one of the gates. Going down into his LCF (launch control facility) he was stunned to find all ten Minuteman missiles "offline." They were all showing a red light which meant "not functioning." He was told that this had happened the night before in conjunction with the UFO sighting.

This situation was highly unusual, as he put it, because they were used to, at most, only one missile being offline at a time for maintenance. And they were proud of their uptime rating of over ninety-five percent. Upon returning to the top side of the facility, he was told never to talk about what had happened, to his wife or ANYONE, and to sign a document to that effect.

When the repair crews came to restart the missiles, he couldn't even tell them what had happened the night before. He never said a word for thirty years. As he put it, he was "embedded in the shell of silence." It wasn't until he found out about another former missile launch officer, Captain Robert Salas, now retired, who served at Malmstrom AFB in Great Falls, Montana and had a similar experience to Schindele's in 1967, that he realized his incident wasn't isolated. (Schindele is the author of *It Never Happened, Volume 1: U.S. Air Force UFO Cover-up Revealed.* 2017)

In fact, this type of incidence happened all across the so-called "Northern Tier" of U.S. strategic bases in 1966-67, and again in 1974-75, including Loring, Wurtsmith, and Ellsworth Air Forces bases. To learn more about these incidents see Robert Hasting's book and video.

Many missiles were tampered with or taken off-line, seemingly by directed electromagnetic impulses from unidentified objects sometimes referred to as "enemy helicopters" and other extremely weird objects. Even though they were officially called "helicopters" — because they hovered by nuclear missile storage areas— in some instances they moved away at over 600 miles per hour, beyond the capacity of even today's most advanced helicopters. A report by Boeing could not identify the cause of the missile failures at Malmstrom. Despite investigations by all branches of the federal government's intelligence agencies, no source for these intrusions was ever identified and no one was ever prosecuted.

[Video available for this chapter.]

Citizen Hearing panel

Panel listens to testimony

Panel asks questions of witnesses

Citizen Hearing witnesses

Chapter Three—My Childhood Encounter with an Unexplained Aerial Craft

In the mid-1970's during summer vacation, I went with my mother to the Florida Everglades to do some bird watching. We were hiking around in the Everglades National Park one afternoon in a marshy area. I looked up overhead and saw something that, to my eyes looked like a full moon. Except it was greenish. Thinking it was odd, I said to my Mom, "*look at the Green Moon! It looks weird.*" Not taking her eyes off the bird she was looking at through her binoculars she said calmly, "*the moon is over there*" and pointed. It was in a completely different part of the sky.

I then looked back at the large object overhead. It was just stationary in the sky and had a kind of ominous feeling. It didn't have definite edges and just felt like it didn't belong there. I then lifted my binoculars to take a better look, as did my mother, and I could see a Z-shaped pattern of dots on the underside of what seemed like a flat surface. It didn't look like the moon anymore. All of a sudden the thing moved in a definite direction and vanished in a nearby cloud. What was that? I couldn't figure it out.

We then went to a park ranger talk, common at National Parks. But the electricity in the whole area had gone out. We told the people sitting next to us about our sighting, and it turned out they had seen the same thing. After the talk, we went up to the park ranger to tell her about our experience, and she just listened and stared at us like we were out of our minds.

This is an experience I will never forget. I even made a pencil drawing of the object which my mother saved. Even when I looked at the picture around the year 2000, it still looks like a UFO. Though at the time of the sighting, I had probably only read one UFO-type book in my life, *The Mothman Prophecies* by John Keel published in 1975. This haunting book is about strange events around the town of Point Pleasant, West Virginia right before the collapse of the Silver Bridge in 1967. Even though I enjoyed the book, it certainly wasn't a topic that most young teenagers would be obsessed with: I certainly wasn't.

Even all these years later, I can remember the feeling of seeing that object in the Florida Everglades. And it still feels weird. To my young mind, that object just didn't belong there next to a cloud in the Florida sky.

Apart from reading Keel's book and having that experience in the Everglades when I was eleven years old, I had absolutely no other experiences with this type of phenomena that I can remember for a long time. It wasn't until I was in college in Amherst, Mass, at Hampshire College that I was taking a photography course. I carried my Olympus manual SLR camera around to catch a good shot.

One day I was out taking a walk on the weekend when I saw a fighter jet from a nearby Air Force base making some crazy turns and a lot of noise. I took a few shots of it as it made tight circles in the sky. When I developed the film at the college's darkroom, I could see what looked like a small disc off the edge of one of the plane's wings. The disc was in several frames at different locations to the jet, so I could rule out a speck of dust on the film as a cause. What could the disc be?

A few years later I happened to come across Timothy Goode's *Above Top Secret,* in a local bookstore. I read it cover to cover. It was great stuff but that was the extent of my interest in the subject. I never once heard anyone mention the topic during my entire college or graduate education. Not once. It was a non-issue.

Witnesses at Farsight

It wasn't until I heard Courtney Brown mention the idea of **Remote Viewing** on the radio in Boulder, Colorado, in 1996 that the subject resurfaced for me. I found his claims so unbelievable that I almost wanted to take his class as a skeptic.

And then, having discovered that remote viewing truly "worked" for the average person, I began teaching at the Farsight Institute for Remote Viewing and encountered several people who had worked for NASA and knew about the UFO subject.

One was a film specialist from Los Angeles, John, who had converted NASA's 16-millimeter film of the Moon landings into video format. He told me you could easily see ancient buildings, domes, and structures in the film. It was apparent, he said, from the film he had seen.

Then there was a man who had been in the astronaut training program and had almost been on one of the shuttle missions. He showed me a NASA group photo of shuttle astronauts with him in the middle. He talked about a secret triangular craft the U.S. government had in its arsenal that could go anywhere on Earth in half an hour, and intricate details about Reagan's Star Wars space weapons program. He also mentioned what he referred to as a "secret space program." At the time this was entirely new information for me. I had been an assistant professor teaching statistics at a state university just a few years before where such topics were never mentioned at all. And those two individuals seemed humble, sincere, and credible to me. I had no way to know if what they were saying was true. Yet their information was shocking in some sense. And it seemed like they had no one to talk to about their secret knowledge.

Furthermore, I hadn't asked them to share this information; they had done so on their own like they needed to talk to someone about it. Neither of them had written any books on the subject, nor given any interviews. They had nothing to gain from talking about what they'd seen except the positive feeling of telling the truth to another human being instead of staying silent.

And that quality also describes all witnesses in this book. They seem highly credible to me and also humble and somewhat shy about talking about what they've seen.

They just want to share their story with someone who will listen carefully to what they're saying and not be judgmental about it. They want to tell the truth.

Because what they're talking about is another type of reality than what we're used to. So the average person could listen to them and then totally forget about what they had just heard. This makes their testimony both credible and simultaneously rare and unbelievable: a true Black Swan Ghost phenomenon.

Brilliant blue object

In 2000, I was at the Rocky Mountain UFO Conference in Laramie, Wyoming. There was a man there by the name of Dr. Steven Greer, founder of the Disclosure Project and CSETI (Center for Study of Extraterrestrial Intelligence), who offered to lead a skywatch after the event. Eighty or so people signed up.

I was naturally skeptical that we would see anything with that many people. We did Dr. Greer's trademark meditation in the afternoon: to use our imagination to locate, view, and vector in any ET craft that could come by later in the evening. He called it "Remote Viewing Squared."

And then at dusk, we proceeded to a location about an hour North of Laramie where the event would supposedly occur. I thought nothing would happen. I was wrong.

About forty-five minutes after we were out in the beautiful Wyoming summer's evening, a thunderstorm appeared and then cleared up. A few moments later, a solid blue light appeared in the sky overhead, about a mile up perhaps. It moved slowly and quietly over us, brightened and then released a brilliant blue beam of light for a few seconds right down on our group. You could have read a book: it was that bright. It looked like a laser beam at a rock concert! But it felt weird too. In a calm but loud voice, Dr. Greer said not to panic: it was just a "group scan." But by whom? Then all of a sudden, it was gone. I had an extraordinarily strange feeling for a few days. Had I just been near a real extraterrestrial craft?

Someone recently asked me by email why I didn't take a photo of the object. Well, let me tell you, the shock you feel when seeing something so bright blue and unusual in the sky is enough to make you forget about everything else for a few seconds. You'll only think about taking a picture after the adrenalin rush has subsided. It's not like the object is there for very long. The closest I can describe the feeling I had is, almost like I was hit by something energetic and powerful. It's a physical feeling and one that only accompanies events that you experience that are very out of the ordinary.

Triangle over Laughlin, NV

In 2001 I was invited to give a presentation on the topic at the UFO Congress held bi-annually in Laughlin, NV. After several years of going over to the U.K., I had obtained conclusive proof that people really could make quite intricate and complex crop circles and formations. And this is what I presented to the audience, along with researcher Colin Andrews.

One night, Denny Clark, another crop circle researcher at the conference, and I decided to do a skywatch at nearby Christmas Tree Pass, a few miles to the West. Driving back at about 1 AM, we were about a mile or two out of town, coming down the hill with the whole city of Laughlin clearly in view.

Denny, all of a sudden, said to me "What's that over the hotel?" I looked and clear as day was a big black triangle moving North above the river right over the hotels along the strip.

I pulled my Ford Explorer over to the side of the road, hoping to get some video. The object moved relatively slowly to the North. It seemed to be about the size of a large commercial airliner but was triangular, dark, no lights, and silent. We could see it because of the bright light coming up from the hotels along the strip.

This could have easily been an experimental military vehicle perhaps, but why was it flying low over hotels in a populated city?

Yet another flying triangle

A few years later, I decided to go camping with my dog on Labor Day in the Snowy Mass Range just West of Laramie, WY. The National Forest campsites were pretty crowded, but eventually I found a spot facing the North East. As night came, I decided to do my own skywatch. I had a pair of 1st-generation Russian-made night binoculars: not great as there was no ability to zoom, but they did amplify low-light objects.

Looking over the area just North West of Laramie, all of a sudden, I saw three lights moving together a mile high or so over the plains. Was it one object or three separate ones? I quickly grabbed the night vision binocs off the hood of my Explorer, switched them on, and took a look.

What I was looking at seemed like one solid, triangular object with bright lights at each of the three vertices of the triangular shape. That was the shape formed by the three lights, but I couldn't see the object itself at such a distance. If so, it had to be pretty big. It seemed to be about five miles away, at a rough guess, and at my elevation. I watched it move quickly to the North and out of sight.

I have to point out that none of these personal sightings can be identified. But they were and still are anomalous to me. How are we to make sense of such sightings? And what about when a large group of people witnesses such a craft and there is still no plausible, official explanation?

But before we go on to see how disruptive such events can be, let's first take a look at the origin of our modern sense of social and physical continuity.

Chapter Four—The Idea of Locality in Modern Science

Around 500 hundred years ago, our current form of science came into being, a forward-looking enterprise based on observation, new ideas, collaboration, and measurement. While the Aristotelean point of view was based on argument and logic alone, the new point of view was evidence and experiment-based. A lot of inventors and creative thinkers pushed this new paradigm forward, often at great personal expense to themselves. The new modern view replaced religious superstitions and paganism and became a powerhouse of ideas and economic transformation, a new way of life that we now take for granted.

And it had one major idea that transcended all these sciences: the idea of locality. Things exist in specific local times or places; they interact linearly, with rules we can understand. Locality underpinned physics, chemistry, biology, everything. It allows for precise linear control that can steer your car or send a space probe to Mars. Very powerful indeed.

Together with modern methods of measurement and mathematical precision, the scientific method reigned for several centuries. With the advent of quantum mechanics in the early 20th century, a new idea was introduced that threatened the underpinnings of this paradigm: the idea of non-locality or "spooky action at a distance," as Einstein called it.

While the foundation of particle physics, this idea threatens classical ideas about time, space, and the nature of reality. It suggests that interactions can happen instantaneously across any distance, even faster than the speed of light. And while substantiated by John Bell and very recent experiments, many physicists still want to banish it. That seems increasingly hard to do.

But there's more to it than just everyday quantum physics.

Because while many scientists and explorers of consciousness want to use non-locality as a basis for explaining things like ESP, remote viewing, presentience, clairvoyance, and related subjects, classically-trained physicists insist that it won't do such a thing. They tell us that correlations between distant particles don't exchange information; they're just mathematical interactions of extremely short duration. But then the physicists go farther, like George Musser in his recent book *Spooky Action at a Distance,* who says: "None of the evidence for ESP has ever stood up, and the types of nonlocal phenomena under discussion are too subtle to mend minds or sway distant baseball games. And when they do that, they aren't being scientific anymore." This type of thinking, in my view, is just nonsense.

You only have to take a brief look at the field of ESP literature by authors like Russell Targ, Dean Radin, Ed May, Rupert Sheldrake, and the work of PEAR Labs to see that it's the very opposite. There's strong evidence for ESP going back at least 100 years, with experiments getting more robust all the time. The effect itself may be weak in the average person, but it's there. On the order of 4 to 8 percent better than chance, consistently in study after study. The confidence we have with these results is on par with any other scientific result in any subject. The "statistical significance" or confidence in these results is on the order of billions, or even trillions to one that they're due to chance.

As a former statistics university teacher, it's still incomprehensible to me that given the robustness of the ESP data, taken as a whole over the last hundred years or so, it's not even discussed in *Science* Magazine, even though the American Parapsychological Assn. is a subgroup of the American Assn. for the Advancement of Science, its publisher.

We've reached an impasse where science will no longer look at the data. They're afraid of what they might find. So instead of taking a serious look, they'd rather dismiss it without a second thought. Kind of like most scientists and journalists of the day did with the Wright Brothers after some of their first flights around Dayton and Kittyhawk, NC.

Richard Wiseman is a psychologist who has done extensive research on this topic and accepts that remote viewing data, as a whole, prove ESP is real. Nonetheless, he argues that because this subject challenges existing science orthodoxy, we should require it to supply more than the usual amount of proof beyond what physics would typically require.

There's something more going on than simply a refusal to look at the data: it's fear of the unknown. Scientists fear losing their funding, status, their stature, and position in society. Once the harbinger of progressive change, science is now the biggest obstacle to our complete understanding of reality. How ironic. As one researcher told me, he presented his ESP data to a colleague who then responded: "It's probably true, but if I admitted that, I'd have to change my whole belief system."

We've come across new territory with this subject area, but we're refusing to even look at any of it so far. The simple fact is that in a debate or courtroom, ESP would win hands down. So it's not for lack of data that we're not taking these subjects seriously.

What's at stake here is a mindset that refuses to change. Its adherents have set up a virtual Maginot

Line to keep out the barbarians. But just as the French attempted to do to the Germans before WWII, the Germans went around it. And now it's started to happen. Because the longer the elephant stays in the room, the longer he'll stay. Modern science, big science at institutions, is at risk of becoming irrelevant because it's pushing away more and more good data. And when the collapse happens, it's likely to be swift and devastating because there are bigger elephants in the room that will become noticed.

In the long run, a whole range of subjects that were previously considered to be "paranormal" will all of a sudden seem normal. Cold Fusion, ETs, UFOs, ghosts: take your pick. I want to argue here that it's all going to be seen as real all of a sudden. And if the experts and scientists were wrong about ESP, what else are they wrong about now?

What if the entire story of our society and civilization is a myth? The myth that humans are the supreme consciousness of the planet; that we're the "top dog" predator on Earth. What if there's something else here too? What if we're not alone? And the other entities have been hiding in plain sight the whole time?

We've never seriously considered the prospect of "extraterrestrial" intelligent life here on Earth, which has never been formally acknowledged before except in folktales. Science attempted to banish it from existence, but it never completely went away. Now it's coming back. It's only a matter of time before we encounter these entities.

Chapter Five—Black Swan Ghosts

Most of us get up every day imagining the world will pretty much be the same as yesterday with only minor, superficial differences. Perhaps it would take too much mental energy to contemplate all the possibilities. And yet, sometimes, unexpected things happen that shake up that view.

In *The Black Swan,* Nassim Nicholas Taleb presents another way to look at things. He shows us that a rare event can happen more frequently than anticipated and that our modern statistical methods are inadequate for predicting such an event. Our whole way of thinking is based on "things as usual" statistics, so we don't know how to deal with the improbable. So when something really out of the ordinary happens, no one sees it in advance. He calls this "Mediocristan" for our shared sense of everyday things. "Extremistan" is the realm of logic for extreme, rare events. When things are falling apart, chains of events interact and produce non-linear outcomes: the effects become disproportionately large compared to the size of the causes.

Think of the catastrophe at the Fukushima reactor in the aftermath of the massive earthquake near there and the resulting Tsunami in Japan, 2009. Simple design decisions made years earlier led to a near-total meltdown after it was damaged. And the cleanup is still going on today.

Or the credit crunch of 2008-9, where risky financial products bought and sold by banks and investment firms, credit derivatives mainly derived mortgage-backed securities, became correlated with each other like dominoes in a way that was never seriously imagined. It all came crashing down or would have if the U.S. Government hadn't intervened with a $700 billion bailout. There was much more risk than acknowledged, and the collapse of one firm could have had disproportionate effects on the whole economy if the banking system had been allowed to collapse.

Those are Black Swan events, rare, with disproportionately large impacts, and not foreseeable beforehand. This unforeseeability makes them even more dangerous. These events are rare but accepted as possibilities, even remote ones.

According to Taleb, when we get to the edge of understanding events, we're in something he calls the "**Platonic Fold.**" This mental area is where our thinking is in a "gray zone" because we don't have any prior experience with that type of event. In the Platonic Fold, we find the Black Swan Ghosts: events that are not only rare but not talked about for any variety of reasons. Events about which we're silent and afraid to discuss. Events that, if accurate, could shatter our whole sense of reality as we've come to know it.

"The Platonic fold is the explosive boundary where the Platonic mindset enters into contact with messy reality, where the gap between what you know and what you think you know becomes dangerously wide. It is here that the Black Swan is produced." (Nassim Nicholas Taleb, *The Black Swan: Second Edition*)

Now let's take another class of events. These are also rare. They are also Black Swan events. But they are not accepted as real for the most part because they are not on most peoples' radar. We might think that a meteor collision with the Earth is exceptionally remote but still possible. But how about a mass UFO landing? A herd of Bigfoot invading your town? A hoard of vampires approaching from the East?

Our social consensus would consider these either as extremely rare OR unreal to the extent that they're not worth seriously considering. These events probably haven't happened in living memory, anyone's memory. (Though some books describe supposedly actual zombie events throughout history.) No one indeed expects them. And yet . . . These are what I call **Black Swan Ghosts**. Rare events that society has not accepted yet as even being possibly real. They are the stuff of movies and fiction but not taken seriously in national newspapers. Our memory of them is almost entirely derived from fiction, and they are said to be imaginary.

You might dismiss these types of phenomena as being the stuff of the supernatural. But it's important to remember that in the Middle Ages, simple vacuums in glass tubes were also considered "supernatural." Aristotle had said that voids were unnatural and didn't exist in nature. Entire experiments and theses had to be put forward to show that vacuum spaces were, in fact, natural. Hundreds of people participated in these experiments that eventually led to our idea of modern science, where people collaborate and test others' ideas and evidence. (David Wootton, *The Invention of Science.*)

Black Swan Ghosts would be considered closer to science fiction than science fact by almost all major institutions and public opinion.

But what if these phenomena are considered authentic by a small fraction of society and imaginary by the rest, by everyone else who still believe what they're told in school or by the media. There are plenty of credible people who've described UFO encounters and even occupants who came out of the craft on the ground.

We're not just talking about individual people but groups of State Patrol officers on the Taconic Parkway who witnessed a large flying black triangle in New York state in the 1980's, for example (see Hynek,

Imbrogno, and Pratt *Night Siege: The Hudson Valley UFO Sightings*). Are these imaginary or real? What if they're possible and have happened, or are happening, but we're totally unprepared for how to think about them. The *Super Black Swan Event* is considered unreal, impossible, and completely unexpected yet suddenly brought into mass consciousness. So Black Swan Ghosts can eventually lead to Super Black Swan events: so unpredictable that they can create mass unrest, panic, or even collapse of existing society.

It's happened before to indigenous societies that encountered European explorers and the countries and kingdoms backing them.

If you think that the scientific community can make sense of these rare events or facts, they can't. As Taleb says:

"Empirical researchers have found evidence that scientists too are vulnerable to narratives, emphasizing titles and "sexy" attention-grabbing punch lines over more substantive matters. They too are human and get their attention from sensational matters." (p. 213 *The Black Swan: Second Edition*)

The difference between ordinary Black Swan events and Black Swan Ghosts is that we have the language to talk about them with the former. We can talk about possible floods, economic crashes, and even the extreme consequences of meteorite impacts.

But what about extraterrestrial first contact? How

do we even begin to think about that event and its consequences? Do we even have words to describe extraterrestrial life, how they think, what's important to them? The movie "Arrival" (2016) dealt in detail with such issues.

We have a whole set of industries built around insuring people from risk. It's an ancient business model. We can insure you for risk of fire, theft, floods, and rare economic events if you're a business. From liability to lawsuits, in case your fleet of ships sink, your airplanes crash or against auto accidents. These are rare events that have defined risk.

And there are entire options markets for stock, commodity, and currency volatility and risk.

Social blindness

But what about events that don't have a defined risk? Events that are so far out of our sense of reality that we don't even know how to talk about them? Events which no one even acknowledges are real? Because these events are so difficult to understand, let alone quantify, no one will officially recognize them. So you're left on your own and maybe even accused by your local media or authorities of having a mental illness.

This is what **social blindness** is all about: denial

of elephants in the room. It doesn't just apply to paranormal events. It describes social processes that every society goes through, from civil rights to acknowledging that certain groups are being abused or discriminated against. Many things we take for granted today at another time were considered unreal or unbelievable. Take child abuse, for example. There was a time before 1962 where it wasn't regarded as real. Doctors couldn't conceive of the idea that parents could do that to their children. The injuries were thought to be caused by falls from trees or neighborhood bullies.

According to Wikipedia: "The whole of recorded history contains references to acts that can be described as child abuse or child maltreatment, but professional inquiry into the topic is considered to have begun in the 1960s. The 1962 publication of the article "The Battered Child Syndrome" by pediatric psychiatrist C. Henry Kempe represents the moment that child maltreatment entered mainstream awareness. Before the article's publication, injuries to children—even repeated bone fractures—were not commonly recognized as the results of intentional trauma. Instead, physicians often looked for undiagnosed bone diseases or accepted parents' accounts of accidental mishaps such as falls or assaults by neighborhood bullies." (Wikipedia entry on child abuse)

So even something as unfortunately commonplace

today as child abuse was not seen as real just a little more than fifty years ago.

The sociologist Ron Westrum calls this a "**hidden event**." It's an event that's repeatedly happening, but no one wants to talk about it because of the consequences to their career or social standing in their community.

And to give another example, there was a time when meteorites were considered unreal: all of them. Why? The French Academy of Sciences had investigated meteorites and had concluded, as had none other than Sir Isaac Newton, that meteorites were an impossibility. Boyle and Lavoisier also shared Newton's doubts about meteorites. As Lavoisier was said to exclaim: "Stones cannot fall from the sky because there are no stones in the sky!" And President Thomas Jefferson pronounced: "I would sooner believe that two Yankee professors would lie than that stones would fall from heaven!" And all the meteorites across France, except one too heavy to move, were rounded up and thrown away. Except there was one problem: stones really do fall from the sky as witnessed several years later by hundreds of residents in the town of L'Aigle, France on April 26, 1803. Thousands of meteorites fell on the town in one night, forever banishing the idea that they don't exist. The Academie Francaise created a commission to study the event, finally recognizing that they were real. In the end, the evidence for meteorites overcame thousands of years of belief, since the time of Aristotle, that nothing changed in the Heavens.

The Boulder Flood of 2013

In late September 2013, I was in Boulder, Colorado. I had just dropped my girlfriend off at the Denver airport when it started drizzling. Then there was continuous rain over the weekend in large amounts. And it didn't stop for a whole week. An unusual weather pattern stayed stationary over the Northern Colorado area, and it dumped at least twenty inches of water on the area in a short time. More rain fell in three days than any recorded month since record-keeping began in 1897.

The flooding was horrendous. Buildings washed away or were severely damaged, cars were destroyed, basements flooded, and some streets turned to rivers. I saw an entire storage unit structure that housed multiple units lifted off the ground and moved several feet. People got into spats with their neighbors by setting up barriers to keep the water from coming down the streets like small rivers. There were just not enough places for the water to go.

We were later told that this was a "500-year flood," something that would not be seen except twice a millennia. That means that no one alive had ever seen something like this before.

This would be an example of a Black Swan event. Catastrophic and very rare yet believable.

The day after Disclosure

Now, let's take something even more extreme. Just for fun, let's imagine an event where the President of the United States announces the discovery and evidence for the existence of extraterrestrials. We don't have any precedent for such an event, so it's totally outside the realm of what we have ever experienced. Since there's no prior experience of this event, there's also no social or cultural reference frame. And with the amount of information technology everywhere, the speed at which such an announcement and become widely known could happen would create spectacularly unpredictable effects within our society. Kind of like a sonic boom created by fast aircraft as they reach and surpass the speed of sound.

Richard Dolan and Bryce Zabel explored this scenario in their book *AD After Disclosure: The People's Guide to Contact* (2012). It would be hard to calculate the effects of such an event, but even if a small percentage of people stayed home, like truck drivers, for any length of time, it would have significant, detrimental, and unpredictable effects on the economy.

Because there are so many unknowns in this scenario, we can't even begin to calculate the costs of such an event. We would be in entirely uncharted territory. And for that reason alone, there's minimal public discussion of this type of event. It stays in the realm of fiction and movies.

Fall of the Berlin Wall

In 1989, I worked at an East-West scientific organization in Vienna: The Institute for Applied Systems Analysis (IIASA), initially set up by Richard Nixon and Leonid Brezhnev during the cold war to foster scientific cooperation between the two countries. I got to know some of the East Germans working next to me. They told me how comfortable their society was to live in if you had the right relationship with the Communist party. They espoused how they had free child care, health care, comfortable apartments, and economic security. And yet, within five months, their society had ceased to exist. By December 1989, the Berlin Wall had fallen, and East Germany was no more.

Was it because the East German government decided to take it down the Wall? No, it was due to false reports from an Italian TV station that border guards were, for the first time, letting people across the Wall to visit relatives in West Berlin. It caused such an enormous mob to gather at the Wall that the East German government had no choice but to let people through to West Berlin by the thousands. And more and more people kept crossing over from the Eastern part of the city to the Western side. And that was, in effect, the end of East Germany.

Everyone knew this would happen someday, but if you had asked political experts about when it would happen, they would have all told you that type of Black Swan event was at least five to ten years away.

Will it be any different with UFO disclosure? We're pretty confident that we know when future events will occur and how they will play out, but in fact, we're no different than the East Germans I knew in 1989. We think things will stay the same forever. But we also all know they don't.

And the reason UFO disclosure will have a proportionately higher impact than the dissolution of the Soviet Union and Bloc because it's not taken seriously; it's not talked about in the mainstream media as a potentially real event. So no one even knows how to talk about it. There's no vocabulary, no assessment of the possible impact on the modern human mind. In short, there's almost no one except a handful of researchers and authors on the subject, and perhaps a handful of people in governmental special access programs who see it coming.

And yet, the evidence for this phenomenon is there. All you have to do is look for it. But this evidence is precisely what Taleb calls "Silent Evidence." Even the Air Force's Project Blue Book, which ascribed nearly every report to weather balloons and meteorites, admitted it couldn't explain five percent of the sightings it received. And that was only the declassified section of Blue Book that the public had access to. Reports that might impact national security were not even included in Blue Book but were part of the CIRVIS (Communications and Reporting of Vital Intelligence Signals) internal reporting system until 2011. These CIRVIS reports have never been declassified in the United States, only Canada. (See Paul Dean's excellent blog documenting decades of NORAD and Air Force reports of UFOs, uncovered through Freedom of Information Act requests, in around Strategic Air Command and Department of Defense installations.)

So how much silent evidence is out there? We don't know. And because there's so little public discussion of this subject, it remains a perpetual information void.

Chapter Six—Conspiracies of Silence

It's not just the government that doesn't want to talk about UFOs and ETs. Our public consciousness doesn't want to talk about it either.

When people speak of the silence surrounding the topic of UFOs and the possibility of extraterrestrials, they often want to blame our federal government for not coming forward with more information. Perhaps that's the case.

The late Dr. Edgar Mitchell, the sixth astronaut to walk on the Moon, reportedly told retired Air Force officer George Filer that NASA had made him sign a document stating he would never say he had seen ETs on the moon or during his flight. And how many others have signed similar non-disclosure agreements, whether they are missile control launch officers, serve on a Naval battleship, or fly planes for the Air Force. There's no doubt the government and its various branches coerce people who've had experiences not to talk about them.

Yet, I often think there is more going on than simply government censorship from alleged national security concerns. Because if ordinary people are demanding the truth as they did during the Watergate hearings for the early 1970's, there would be a new, official investigation of this topic.

But they aren't. There hasn't been a national discussion on the topic since the one-day Congressional hearings in 1968. Our society is content to ignore this question and leave it in a state of limbo.

The structure of secrecy

As Eviatar Zerubavel makes clear in his book, *The Elephant in the Room*, silence is an active state of denial, not a passive one:

"Like silence, denial involves active avoidance. Rather than simply failing to notice something, it entails a deliberate effort to avoid noticing it. Furthermore, it usually involves refusing to acknowledge the presence of things that beg for attention, thereby reminding us that conspiracies of silence revolve not around those largely unnoticeable matters we simply overlook but, on the contrary, around those highly conspicuous matters we deliberately try to avoid." (p. 53)

However, the conspiracies of silence Zerubavel

refers to usually have to do with pain, shame, and fear: topics like sexual violence, abuse, and atrocities like the Holocaust. However, in this case, we're dealing with such a level of fear about the unknown that we can't even talk about it. We don't even know what we don't know about the phenomena. It's just a big mystery box.

When it comes to the UFO phenomena, this type of silent avoidance is so loud; you can't miss it. It's the ultimate elephant in the room. "The closer one gets to it, the more pressure one feels to deny its presence." (p. 54)

Some of the people closest to this phenomenon have served in the military and intelligence services who've come smack up against pieces of extraterrestrial material or entire crafts and their occupants. Even if they didn't mind facing the ridicule of their neighbors and friends, they've signed security agreements forbidding them from ever talking about it again with anyone, including other people who witnessed the same event. So they're in a deep double bind.

I'd argue this type of silence creates enormous risks for our society, on par with the credit default of 2008 or greater. Should credible evidence be presented to the public, what's likely to happen is an information cascade of unknown proportions. It will grow so quickly that the shock's social, cultural, and economic effects will be unpredictable.

It doesn't have to be this way. Other countries like Russia, China, and several Latin American countries like Brazil, Peru, and Uruguay take the subject seriously enough to release accurate information to the public. Some even have occasional conferences about the topic or openly involve their military in investigating important contact cases and UFO hotspots. China has a national UFO society, and citizens must have a state license to be an investigator of the subject.

The United States alone continues to ignore the subject, ridicule witnesses and let the mainstream media just mock the whole thing. It's a deplorable, childish, inexcusable state of affairs.

In the upcoming chapters, we'll hear from witnesses to this phenomenon. We don't know what they've experienced, and they don't either. But the first step is to listen to their stories with open ears and minds and without judgment.

I think you'll quickly see that these peoples' encounters cannot be explained by the planet Venus, flocks of geese, or swamp gas. Something much more profound is going on, and I'm confident that neither you or I understand even a small part of it.

Chapter Seven—Peter: Sighting of Object and Humanoid, Strange Phone Call, and Mysterious UFO Organization

During my visits to the U.K. for crop circle tours and research, I came across a man named Peter in one of the pubs near Beckhampton, a short distance from the market town of Marlborough in Wiltshire. This pub is so old that Charles Dickens is said to have visited it many times on his way from London to the ancient Roman town of Bath in the Southwest of Britain.

Peter is a jockey, small in stature but big in spirit. I don't remember when I first heard his story, but we used to visit this pub on a crop circle tour led by Ron Russell: one time, Peter was there sitting at the bar, and our group got started talking to him. He told us the most riveting story of his night-time encounter with an unexplained object, an unidentified being, and a mysterious organization.

I've heard Peter recount this story many times now, and he's allowed me to video and tape-record him talking about it. It's been the same story for about twenty years that he told me. I can tell you that Peter believes it.

Here's how Peter tells it:

He and a friend were walking over the downs near Epsom in Surrey carrying a gold-embossed bust of a Native American to put in storage. Peter had always been interested in Native American culture since he was young. It was about 11:20 PM and completely dark. They had decided to take a shortcut over the downs. The area was highly secluded.

As they crossed the deserted fields, Peter says he saw a bluish light getting closer and closer. Then, making a whirring sound, it started a vertical descent to the hill closest to them, about a hundred yards away. As it got closer to the ground, a bright blue light flashed every five seconds, illuminating the disc's shape, with a blue haze around it, outlined in the darkness.

It landed, and a door opened on the side after a few minutes. Peter and his friend were frozen in their tracks with excitement and fear. Having had some

UFO sightings as a kid in his town, Peter was excited and fascinated. His friend was petrified.

It turns out that in the 1960's Peter had seen an object hovering over his town, as had many other residents. He said it had windows, and the occupants were waving at him. He had always felt they were friendly.

Now, he felt like they were returning for him, right at this moment, to take him to the stars.

The door on the side of the craft opened, and a very tall being in a skin-tight suit emerged and started walking towards him and his friend. The being had a small red flashlight or an object that emitted red light in its left hand.

Peter wanted to walk towards the being, but his friend had a panic attack and was trying frantically to pull Peter away from the being and object. The friend wet his pants and kept pulling on Peter.

Peter says that he was sure these were the same type of beings he had observed in the sky as a kid, and he wanted to make contact right then and there. But as his friend became more panicky, so did Peter. The being got within 20 meters of them. His friend said: "He's got a ray gun; let's get out of here!" They inadvertently dropped the Indian bust and started to run.

Peter and his friend kept running until they came to a road and waved down the first car that approached. It turned out to be some of their friends. They quickly explained what had just happened. Their friends were skeptical and thought they must be drunk.

They could see the craft lift off and hover over the ground from the car, with the stroboscopic blue light pulsing every few seconds, silhouetting the craft. After it was a distance over the ground, it started to move and then shot off over the horizon instantly.

Peter insisted they be taken to a police station to report the sighting. Peter explained that there were official UFO reporting forms at local police stations in those days.

Peter said they got to the nearest station before 1 AM, and there was stereotypical Bobby (British term for policeman) drinking a cup of tea sitting at the front desk. The Bobby asked them what was going on. Pete, his friend, and the folks who picked them up were all very excited. The Bobby said: "All right, everyone, calm down. What's going on?." They explained what they had seen, and he said: "Here, fill out this form." It was an official UFO reporting form.

Peter filled out the form, which he said asked for all sorts of details about what had been observed. (Back in the 1970's the Ministry of Defense did indeed have official UFO reporting forms at police stations for witnesses to fill out.) They left the police station at around 1 AM.

Having to work the next day, Peter went back to

Manchester later that day; a few hours drive away. According to Peter, his friend was so scared by the event that he locked himself in his room and barred the door with furniture for a week and only opened the door to let his Mom bring him food and use the bathroom.

Peter later went back to look for the Indian bust where they had dropped it, but it was not there.

Peter arrived at work at 6 AM the following day and at 6:15, fifteen minutes later, Peter received a phone call. He asked who was calling.

"**Never mind who I am. About that UFO you saw last night, it was a weather balloon.**"

Peter retorted into the phone, "That was not an [expletive deleted] weather balloon."

The voice on the phone said: "**I'm telling you, you saw a weather balloon. Now keep your mouth shut.**"

Pete said he responded: "What I saw last night was no weather balloon," and he slammed down the phone.

The next day, at work again, Peter received a letter. It purported to be from a local UFO research organization. Now Peter explained to me that in those days of the early 1970's it took local mail a few days to get across town. But this letter was unbelievably there just a day after his sighting.

The letter said there would be a UFO conference

the following week in his town and that he was invited. He had to get permission from his boss to go, and he did.

On the appointed date, Peter made his way across Manchester to the address given in the letter. It turned out to be a pub curiously enough. He asked the pub owner if there was a UFO meeting there. The owner said: "I don't know about that, but there are a group of men downstairs."

Peter went downstairs and tried to open the door to a large room. It was locked. Then the door opened and the man opening it said: "**Come in, we've been waiting for you.**" As Peter described it, about thirty men were seated around a table, all wearing the same white uniform, like a lab coat. Peter said that every nationality was represented there, from every continent. "It was like a meeting of the United Nations."

Peter sat down and asked if this was the UFO conference. The group leader responded: "**We want to hear about your sighting Peter.**"

Peter was a bit disappointed, thinking he would hear other peoples' stories but proceeded to tell the men about the object and the tall being that walked towards him. The men periodically asked him questions, very particular ones. They asked him to draw what he had seen. Peter said: "they wanted to know about every blade of grass, every detail."

This questioning went on for three hours. And at

the end, the group leader finally said: "**What you saw was a weather balloon.**"

They asked Peter for his drawings, and he was then dismissed from the room. Everyone else stayed. That was the last he heard about the event. It never appeared in the local newspaper. And no one ever contacted him again.

I've heard Peter tell this story about ten times with the same emotion and tension, and it's been consistent each time. I have no doubt he believes in the account he's told me and others.

[Video available for this chapter.]

Peter—witness to unexplained craft and humanoid occupant

Chapter Eight—Louise: Huckleberries, Flying Disc, and US Military Response

Louise Voves is a woman I met in North Idaho, a friend of another witness in this book, Joy French, who had an interest in UFOs after an encounter on Mt. St. Helens that left her and a friend with several hours of missing time (described in the next chapter). I met Louise at Joy's apartment once, and she told me her story. I had a subsequent chance to interview her at her bakery in Athol, ID, in October 2015. Louise passed away due to complications from heart surgery several months after the interview. She was in her mid-80s.

Louise and her brother picked huckleberries once a year. It was in the early 1970's. The brother made Huckleberry pies and jams for a living. So once a year, they trekked out to a national forest near the town of

Usk, Washington, and the Kalispel Indian Reservation, just over the Idaho border. She told me this particular spot had good huckleberries. The huckleberry species *Vaccinium* is endemic to the Idaho and Montana area.

They were out there in late Summer at a known "good spot." A mother and her son were nearby, and some other people were also picking huckleberries. Suddenly, they heard the mother say: *Look, what IS that?* and point up to the sky above them.

Above the pine trees in the area, they all saw what Louise described as *a tortoise shell, round on the top and flat on the bottom with red, green, and yellow-colored lights all around where the two shells meet.* It was wobbling back and forth, basically just hovering in the same spot, about thirty to forty feet across in diameter. The mother and son panicked and started to leave, saying they would get the police.

Louise and her brother watched the object for five to seven minutes. It made a motion like a leaf swaying back and forth as it fell, though this object was stationary. She said the disc suddenly dove towards the ground at about a 45-degree angle and made a whooshing sound. It moved away horizontally and quickly just over the earth and went out of the area. As it did *the object pushed down all the meadow and grasses in its path completely flattening them in a path about 30 feet across or so for one-hundred feet in a straight line.*

They weren't sure what they had just seen. *Louise told me that they didn't even have the word "UFO" in their vocabulary.* After the object had left, they went back to picking Huckleberries.

The mother and son, who had been frightened by the object, made their way down to the town of Usk and visited the police station who had called the sheriff, who in turn called the military. (Spokane has been home to Fairchild Air Force Base since the 1940's, and it was a Strategic Air Command base in the 1970's at the time of Louise's sighting.)

After what seemed like an hour later, a convoy of U.S. Army trucks and tribal police from the nearby Indian reservation showed up at the site where Louise and her brother were. The military personnel dismounted from their vehicles and proceeded to ask Louise and her brother a ton of questions about what they had just seen. They wanted to see precisely where the aerial vehicle went low to the ground and the tracks it had made.

Louise then took the military guys to the track of grasses that the object had flattened, and they were highly interested, some of the soldiers following the path into the distance. They said to her and her brother: "**Were you drinking?**" No, they hadn't been drinking. They then asked Louise: "**Did you see anyone?**" (Implying possible occupants of the flying disc, perhaps.)

Then they said: "**You have to leave the area.**" Louise and her brother were seriously upset about this. She told her friend Joy (featured in the next chapter) that they were told not to talk about what she had seen and may have even been asked to sign something to that effect. As they left, they saw the military guys getting out their equipment, what could perhaps be radiation and soil-testing gear.

As Louis and her brother drove away, more military vehicles arrived at the scene, including troop carriers.

They went back the next day, but now there was a military jeep stationed a few miles from their huckleberry spot and "Kelly humps," tank traps, freshly dug into the road.

As they approached, the soldier in the jeep said: "**No one is allowed in the area; you'll have to go back.**"

This meant that Louise and her brother wouldn't pick as many huckleberries that season, and they were upset about that since her brother already had orders to fulfill. They eventually found another Huckleberry spot. Louise told her friend Joy, whose own strange story is included below that the military told her never to talk about what she had seen. A friend of Louise' attempted to visit the same area a couple of days later and was still not allowed in. Louise said she never saw anything about this incident in the local newspapers or heard about it again.

At the end of our interview, Louise told me: *You know what you saw, and no one can tell you any differently.*

[Video available for this chapter.]

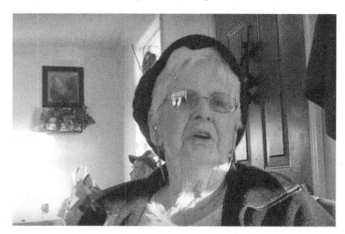

Louise Voves

Chapter Nine—Joy French: Vehicle Stalls, Strange Luminosity, Missing Time with Friend

Joy French is a woman now in her nineties who spent most of her life working for Alaska Airlines in ground support and mechanics: she told me she was two years too late to be a flight attendant. I met Joy in the Coeur D'Alene, Idaho area after she put an ad in the local paper for a meeting of UFO witnesses.

Why did Joy want to assemble such a group?

Joy said that in the 1980's she was living in the Mt. St. Helens area and had an experience there she could never explain.

She had contacted, via Citizen Band (CB) radio, a gay friend of hers, Don, and asked him to share some wine with her in the evening. He also asked her if she wanted to get together to watch a movie together at his place. She agreed to drive down to his residence lower down on the mountain by Lake Merwin.

The last thing she clearly remembers that day is hanging up the mic of the CB, leaving her house, and getting into her vehicle.

The next thing she remembers is that it's dark and both of them are in her car driving up the mountain to her place at around 2 A.M. *Except Don was driving the car and she never, ever let anyone drive her cars!* She told me she was firm about that.

The next thing she remembers is that the radio goes out, and the car stalls suddenly. Her friend, a car mechanic, got out of the driver-side door and went to the vehicle's front. Joy remembers that it should have been pitch black at that location, except her friend was covered in bright light coming from the sky, so bright it was like "daylight at noon," as she put it. She remembers asking him, "where is all that light coming from?"

He lifted the hood and looked inside the engine compartment for a few minutes. He said, "there's nothing wrong with the engine; start it." It started perfectly, and Don closed the hood and got back in the car.

Joy's next memory is waking up in her bed many hours later at about 8 a.m. She has no recall how she got there or where her friend is at this point. She called Don on the CB, and he was back at home. She suggested they should meet down at the community kitchen.

Once they met, she asked him: "What happened last night? Everyone will think we're crazy." He had the same memories as she did and the same missing time gaps. He told her that no one would believe them if they talked about it and agreed that everyone would think they were crazy.

They decided to never talk about it again. Joy kept her word for about a decade.

Joy can't explain what happened to her and her friend to this day. She had some hypnosis, but no memories that she didn't already have surfaced.

Her remedy was to hold "UFO witness meetings" in the Pacific Northwest area, of which I was able to attend three. And these meetings were filled with people who had related experiences from all over Idaho and Washington.

[Video available for this chapter.]

Joy French

Chapter Ten—Retired UK Police Officer Sees Extremely Bright Object and "Spaceman"

In 2010, as part of my crop circle tour to the U.K., we were able to organize a meeting of UFO witnesses in Wales with the help of researcher and author Colin Andrews. Our ten-person group drove out there one day, a three-hour drive from the town of Marlborough where our hotel was, along with Busty Taylor, a private pilot, and early crop circle researcher.

A local researcher there had assembled three witnesses in a small meeting hall. The witnesses included a local woman who had observed an incredibly bright, pulsing light over her vehicle, a former aeronautics engineer who saw an ascending luminous disc right over a tree in his backyard, and a retired policeman who observed an unidentifiable "space being" as he called it. It is the latter case I wish to expound on here.

The former "Bobby" (the British term for policeman) named Ken, who also had been a member of the Royal Air Force, served in Bristol. He told us that one night in 1976, his son had come running into the house saying, "Dad, there's a UFO outside, come take a look." When Ken got outside, he saw that all the neighbors were looking at a strange orange light coming in over the golf course. It was pulsing and seemed very big. Even though the object was not far away, a telescope had been set up, and Ken looked through it: He said the thing was so bright it was "blinding." Ken was off-duty at the time, so when people suggested he immediately investigate, he was happy to decline. Then, the following day as he was driving back from his shift at 6 a.m., he passed the local agricultural college. He turned his head and saw a very tall being in what looked like a spacesuit. Ken said it was at least eight feet tall. Its back was to the wall, and its hands were down and pressed to the wall. He told us it was not human. He was so shocked he kept driving back home and told his wife, "I've just seen a Spaceman!"

She laughed at him most cynically. Yet later that day, the BBC reported the following: a couple, Joyce Bowles and Ted Pratt, were driving the previous night through Chilcomb, near Winchester, when they saw an orange object in the air behind trees along the road. Their car then went out of control and came to rest on a verge by the side of the road. They could see a cigar-shaped object with three beings in the cockpit area. One of them came out, walked right out on the road, and approached the car. He wore a "silvery boilerplate" uniform and had a beard and sideburns. He put his head in the window and looked right at Joyce and then at Ted. He said things to them and made references to fields and crop circles.

He then looked at their dashboard, and the car started up again. Joyce reported that the headlights were four times brighter than usual. The being began to walk behind the car, and then all of a sudden, the being and craft were gone.

The *Daily Mail* reported eight other sightings of a similar-looking craft around the area that weekend and one of "a strange man in a silvery suit."

Joyce and Ted reported a subsequent encounter a few weeks later with the same beings in the same area, followed the next year by yet another meeting by Joyce and a different neighbor, and finally by one that Joyce had by herself. In each case, the beings had messages for Joyce about humanity and the dangers of pollution and warfare for the Earth and its population.

I have to say, listening to Joyce and her companion talk about this incident during an interview, they seem like typical residents of their area and quite sincere in their account of what happened to them.

The researcher Colin Andrews conveyed to me how he and fellow researcher Pat Delgado visited the site of the Bowles/Pratt encounter the following day and saw the tire track marks veering off the road and hedgerow exactly as the witnesses described.

Ken, a retired policeman in the UK who saw a "Spaceman"

Chapter Eleven—Franco and the Glowing Disc over Wonderland Lake

Franco is someone I met through some friends in Boulder, Colorado. He's an electrician who's worked at government labs such as NIST, the National Institute of Standards and Technology. He told me this fantastic story that happened to him on June 6, 2006, at a few minutes past 2 AM. The incident lasted a little over 45 minutes.

He was lying in bed one night when he noticed all the neighborhood dogs barking in the Wonderland Lake area of Northern Boulder. The barking was very loud and intense and seemed to encompass the entire neighborhood of dogs. He went to the window and immediately saw two large, peach-colored, circular lights on the side of a noiseless, quiet object hovering over the lake. Franco remembers that the two peach-

colored lights were at least 30 feet across and sep-
arated by at least 25 feet. The craft appeared to be
at least 100 feet long and wide. However, the lights
obscured a good view of the entire craft.

Franco was able to get some "shadowy" views of
the craft, and it was not circular but compartmentalized. Some of the compartments were very large. The
whole vehicle was floating five or six feet above the
water.

After a few minutes, the object moved away towards the foothills and floated up to the top of one
of the hills. It moved in the opposite direction of his
house in a left-to-right motion across the lake. This
went on for a few minutes, and the dogs were still
barking very intensely. Franco had the feeling that the
object was searching for something.

Then, all the lights disappeared in an instant, and
he thought it was gone. It reappeared at the top of
a ridge in the North Boulder foothills above Wonderland Lake.

It was hovering above the ridge, and the soft,
peach-colored lights were still facing Franco's direction. The craft seemed to sway from side to side as
it hovered for about ten minutes. The dogs were still
barking.

The object moved to the left on the ridge by a
few hundred feet, stopped, and then turned around.
The peach-colored lights were now on the other side,

and Franco could instead see one, deep-red light. The craft gently landed on the ridge. It emitted a thudding sound that Franco could feel in his chest as it appeared to land. There was an eerie feeling. All the dogs in the area suddenly became quiet.

It was dead silent, and as the craft sat there on the ridge, the red light started repeatedly pulsating from brighter to dimmer, and it seemed to be becoming more intense.

Franco got to his laptop and contacted the National UFO Reporting Agency and made a report of the incident. (Franco told me he had left his camera in his truck down the street and didn't want to miss any unfolding events.)

Thirty to forty minutes had passed so far.

The craft seemed to be hovering just above the ground when Franco could hear the unmistakable sound of military jets coming in fast from the North. As the two planes approached the area, the red light on the craft shrunk to become a slight, dim, purple glow.

The craft then shot up in the air in total silence, up at least 2,000 feet above the ridge. The ship then hovered there for about three to four seconds and made a loop that appeared as a circular trace of light.

The craft then stopped for a second and moved off rapidly towards the South East horizon at an incredible speed.

The jets flew overhead at a tremendous pace caus-
ing Franco's windows to rattle.
[Video available for this chapter.]

Franco describes glowing object he saw over Wonderland Lake

House where Franco saw the glowing object

Wonderland Lake where the object was first spotted

Foothills where object moved to before taking off at high speed

Chapter Twelve—Cold Fusion: "Junk Science" or Breakthrough Energy Technology?

The subject of Cold Fusion is developing as I write this, but it's still an obvious example of how establishment science resists and suppresses new ideas. In 1989, Stanley Fleischmann and Pons, on March 23rd, announced that they had discovered table-top "cold" fusion as it's known: something that had previously been associated only with hot fusion devices. These are expensive, hyper-complicated machines that cost billions and attempt to replicate the super-high surface temperature of the sun and the continual fusion reactions that sustain it.

It was thought that it was impossible to reproduce this reaction at lower temperatures, but Fleischmann and Pons were doing just that. And it wasn't expensive. They were electrochemists, not physicists, and they were mercilessly attacked by mainstream scientists, the media, and everyone. Attempts were made to reproduce the experiment with deuterium and palladium. These initially failed, but later attempts were successful using different types of palladium.

The patent office asked MIT to determine if cold fusion were an actual, natural process. MIT did their experiments and reported back that it didn't work. President Bush Sr. formed a working committee to do its investigation. Most of the members, including its chair, were connected to hot fusion. They also reported in the negative.

John Huizenga even wrote a book entitled "Cold Fusion: Science Fiasco of the Century." MIT held a funeral celebration for cold fusion. Fleischmann and Pons fled the United States back to their home countries. It became a witch hunt. Researcher and electrochemist Dr. John O'Meara Bockris was investigated by his university not once but three times for fraud after he detected tritium in his cold fusion experiment: something that indicates a nuclear reaction is going on.

Now, it's clear that Cold Fusion is a sometimes finicky, complex reaction to get going. John O'Bockris said that it sometimes could take hundreds of hours for the reaction to start. That's a long time. But even so, it appears that mainstream science labs like MIT and Cal Tech were pleased for it not to work. However, a small percentage of labs kept reporting positive results, including labs in Israel, the U.S. Navy, all the way up to the present day. However, these have been ignored.

At the 18th meeting of the Society for Scientific Exploration in San Francisco, the keynote speaker was Dr. Vittorio Violante, a hot fusion expert connected with Italy's ENEA, a government energy research institute. Dr. Violante told the audience that though cold fusion is a finicky process demanding precisely the correct chemical elements, it's real, and it works. And he had no interest in this, being a hot fusion researcher. He said the ENEA had determined that it is not a chemical reaction but one based on the principles of resonance. You have to get the correct type of palladium "doped" with just the right amount of other neighboring metals from the periodic table. In other words, the palladium has to have the right amount of surface defects.

As of the writing of this book, a new type of cold fusion called LENR (low energy nuclear reaction or lattice enable nuclear reaction) is being developed. No one is sure exactly why it works but work it does. Stanford Research International (SRI), the same lab that initially conducted classified remote viewing research for the U.S. government back in the 1970s, recently issued a press release in January of 2017 confirming their successful nine-month testing of such a device. It may not even be a type of fusion, technically. But at the sub-atomic level, the elements in the device resonate together to produce a lot of heat and even possibly electricity.

I'm not the only one thinking this way. As of the writing of this book, Bill Gates and other billionaires have formed the Breakthrough Energy Coalition to invest in and develop new, inexpensive, clean forms of energy. On their website, nuclear fusion is listed as one of the energy sources they're studying. Given that Italian Cold Fusion experts have briefed Gates, we know he's interested in both types.

Like other subjects in this book, it's clear that modern science dropped the ball on this topic. Cold Fusion turns out to be a fundamental, natural process that produces inexpensive energy, which could change how we live. And yet it's become just another elephant in the room, something most scientists would like to go away. But like most elephants, it's still in the room and getting bigger.

Chapter Thirteen—Paul and Sonya's Terrifying Encounter with Glowing Humanoids over Silbury Hill

In the mid-1990's Wiltshire residents Paul and Sonya decided to spend a night on Silbury Hill, the largest and oldest manmade Earth mound in Europe, located just south of the town of Avebury. Around this time, you could climb the mound as I've done a few times. However, nowadays, this is punishable by a steep fine, and there is a sign at the bottom warning would-be hikers to stay away.

Paul and Sonya told me that they had climbed there with three friends, two of whom, Kenny and Darrell, left early on to join a skywatch with a group in Avebury. Another friend, Rob, stayed with them on the hill. About five teenagers were "mucking about, being noisy and drinking" who arrived after Paul and Sonya climbed the hill.

They were all listening to electronic music by a band called Eat Static on a cassette player. After 1 AM, all the dogs in the area started barking at once. Sonya noticed an odd smell. She thought she heard whispering sounds and walked over to the hill's edge to see what was going on.

She then said to Paul: "There's something coming up the hill." It had an ominous and terrifying feeling, but nothing was visible. "It was dark and weird; everything seemed to change. It went completely silent as well. It's like everything stopped."

The next odd thing that happened, around 1:30 AM, is that a pea-soup thick wall of fog suddenly appeared around the whole area right below the hill and started to rise to their location. Everyone ran around, pointing their flashlights into the fog-enshrouded darkness.

Suddenly, someone pointed and said: "What's that?" They all noticed some lights in the field immediately to the south of the hill on the other side of the A4 highway. The lights started to move down the field, which made Paul and Sonya think it was an automobile with its headlights on or perhaps a bicycle with flashlights attached. It seemed to be bumping up and down. But as it came down the field in their direction, they noticed it was a few feet over the field and not in it.

As it approached the A4 road, the ball of light split into several balls of light. Each ball seemed to contain a being, sitting in a lotus position, legs crossed. Someone said: "They're little people." Each little person had an orange glowing sphere above it. Sonya had a flashlight that she directed through the fog towards these beings, who then turned mechanically together towards Paul and Sonya. The beings, who appeared to be physical humanoids sitting in illuminated tetrahedral shapes, floated up towards them.

Paul felt a sense of terror, the most extreme he had ever felt in his life. The fear slowly rose from his toes to his head as the lights came closer to him. "I thought I was going to die." His friend Rob did an "Olympic jump" backward as the lights approached. Then, Paul's fear just vanished as abruptly as it had appeared.

Eventually, the lights were high enough to illuminate a large tree below. Paul said they were about ten feet above him. All of a sudden, the whole area just "lit up." Then, just as they had approached, the lights gradually went back down the hill and moved across the A4 road.

But then they noticed a car approaching from the East on the A4. It slowed as it approached the wall of fog. The balls of light collapsed into one light the size of a tennis ball that darted suddenly into a bush next to the road. As the car approached the bush, the ball of light quickly went behind the vehicle.

As it turns out, the car driver, Paul Vigay, a crop circle researcher, now deceased, saw the ball of light too and how it moved behind his vehicle. I heard him talk about this at several lectures where he mentioned it and the thick fog wall, describing the encounter as one of the strangest things he had ever seen in his life.

Ron Russell, an acquaintance who introduced me to crop circles, had a chance to talk with Paul Vigay about this encounter, and he described seeing the wall of fog that Paul and Sonya described and the ball of light that emerged from behind the hedgerow and followed his car for some distance.

Paul and Sonya attempted to wake the sleeping teenagers to show them the lights back up on the hill, but they couldn't stir them.

At the top of the hill, Paul remembers that the ball then reappeared near Silbury in a field to the East. The ball then crossed over the A4 again. Two tiny beings seemed to emerge from the light ball, walked around it, and then got back inside. The ball then became a string of four or five lights that moved in a line up the field directly across from Silbury Hill and to the South West. Paul and Sonya felt like the lights were "scanning" the open field as if they were looking for something.

Someone named Jaime, who had been in a car parked by the side of the road, came up to the top of

Silbury Hill and asked them if they had seen the lights moving up the field. In a state of excitement and panic, Paul and Sonya told him what they had seen and spent the rest of the night at the top of the hill and left the following day. They said that later that day, the British military closed off the entire area around Silbury Hill for two days.

They could never explain what they had seen, nor did they ever meet or talk to Paul Vigay in person. Their friend Rob, who was on the hill with them that night, wouldn't sleep without the lights on for two years afterward.

They developed a sudden interest in music and formed the group ManmadeMan, whose mysterious and electronic "chill" songs you can find today online.

Silbury Hill area as ET portal

Colin Andrews, mentioned above with the Wales UFO witnesses, once described to our crop circle tour group how he learned something secret about the Silbury Hill area, which may explain some aspects of the Paul and Sonya story.

Colin was asked to make a presentation in Arlington, Virginia, in the mid-1990s, which he told me was heavily attended by U.S. intelligence personnel. Among the attendees was a science advisor to a former U.S. President.

One of the presentations was by a well-known U.S. author and researcher who presented slides of crop circles and similar large areas of flattened plants. The audience saw pictures of random shapes and some whole fields created by so-called "lodging," damage to plants caused by wind and rain. Colin said the presentation surprised and baffled him.

Earlier that afternoon, the science advisor approached Colin and told him that there was something he should know, but he could not be seen discussing it with him.

He said: "My wife will ask you for a few minutes later if you would talk to her."

The science advisor's wife approached Colin as the presentation mentioned above was still going on, and they agreed to walk outside into the parking lot, taking Colin's wife with them. The advisor's wife then proceeded to tell them that both the U.S. and U.K. governments monitored a field directly south of Silbury Hill, 24 hours a day, seven days a week, because of UFO activity there. The area was a portal of sorts, and the authorities knew these craft emanated from a location in the North Sea, off the Shetland Islands (North East of Scotland).

It should be noted that this field is directly adjacent to the one where Paul and Sonya saw the lights.

Many years later, Colin was at one of the X-

Conferences held by Steve Bassett and the Paradigm Research Group in Washington, D.C., from 2004 to 2010. The conference's focus was the subject of UFOs and extraterrestrial disclosure.

A man approached Colin and said he had served in the U.S. military as an advisor to an aeronautics company in Wiltshire and particularly enjoyed the Silbury Hill area. He told Colin he was touring the area and went camping just North of Silbury Hill and the nearby village of Avebury one night.

After he had gone to sleep in his tent, he awoke to hear scratching sounds across the roof of his tent. It went on for an uncomfortable period, so he grabbed his flashlight, not knowing what he would see. As he whipped open the door flap, he saw an exceptionally tall being of some kind run away at speed, leaping in huge strides as it sunk back into the dark.

He was so shocked by the encounter that he called his father in the U.S. Later on, twenty minutes after he had returned to his residence in the U.K., two Royal Air Force officials from Lyneham Airfield near Swindon visited him. They showed him a mug book of sorts containing different photos of extraterrestrials and asked him to pick out which one was most similar.

Whether Colin's stories and Paul and Sonya's encounter are related is unknown. But it seems interesting that he had confirmation from a government advisor and military person that something very un-

108

usual was going on in this area.
[Video available for this chapter.]

Silbury Hill, largest and oldest earth mound in Europe, near Avebury, U.K.

Chapter Fourteen—The Costs of Denial

You may have read through this book agreeing with some things I've said but still wondering what the point is. Why does it matter that we deny something in front of our nose? Well, to me, it has to do with our character, individually and as a society. We pride ourselves on being modern, progressive, and open to the truth. We read websites, news sites, blogs daily to inform ourselves on what's going on and the issues in our lives. And yet, we also deny the reality of things happening right in front of us. Such matters confront us every day, such as police brutality, rape on campus, child abuse, and other types of cruelty.

And yet, with this issue, the costs incurred from denying its existence are detrimental to our sense of justice, reality, and the very definition of who we are. It's a little bit like we are tribal people leaving our village for the first time, seeing something out there we can't identify, and then denying we had the experience in the first place.

110

Especially in America, we have a concept of "extending the franchise" to more and more members of society. First, women got the right to vote, and then Black Americans, and then gays were legally allowed to marry. Is the next step to treat people who've had unexplainable encounters more decently and humanely instead of ridiculing and degrading them?

This process is a similar extension of the franchise: to people who have experienced the unknown and should be able to talk about it openly without being denigrated, threatened, ridiculed, and laughed at. So human beings can continue to live with the fundamental human rights of speech, telling the truth, and being able to talk about their experiences, no matter how "out of the ordinary" they seem to be.

At the Citizen Hearing on Disclosure in Spring of 2013, I had a chance to talk to press members. An exasperated New York Times photographer said to me: "This is the best material I've ever seen, but I can't get them [his bosses at the NYT] to send anyone down from New York City to cover it."

After the Citizen Hearing event, I called retired Congressman Merrill Cook of Salt Lake City, Utah, one of the retired representatives who presided over the event. I asked him about his take on the whole thing. He said, though he came into the Hearing as a skeptic, he found the evidence presented at the mock hearing extremely persuasive and thought that, at the very least, it raised the issue of collisions and aircraft safety. Evidently, Mr. Cook was paying attention to the evidence presented. The same is not true of our media.

The Washington Post had sent Alexandra Petri, one of their bloggers. She was there for almost the entire event: I sat in the press section of the National Press Clubroom, so I had a chance to talk with the reporters. However, her piece in the Post on May 3, 2013, "Believe in UFO's? Highlights of the Citizen Hearing on Disclosure," was riddled with sarcasm and a general attitude of "this is not a serious subject." She complains of the whole thing as incomprehensible to her in many ways, but it doesn't look like she put in much effort to understand the witnesses' stories and histories. Her attitude spills off the page: "Who cares? It's just a bunch of weirdos talking about things I don't understand."

Another writer for the Washington Post said she had consulted a psychologist who told her that belief in UFOs is characteristic of "schizotypal mental disorder": part of the schizophrenic range of disorders. The latter's core features are "reality distortion" associated with a lack of ability to socialize with others, social anxiety, paranoia, and belief in the occult, "magical thinking." Also included are beliefs in unconventional ideas that are "inconsistent with subcultural norms"

(whatever that means: we're told it's "superstitious-
ness, belief in clairvoyance, telepathy, or 'sixth sense';
in children and adolescents, bizarre fantasies or preoc-
cupations"). Is this beginning to sound tautological?

Someone who's had an experience with something that is not culturally accepted is most likely to
have their cultural belief systems changed. You'd be
surprised by how many people who've encountered
the unknown report a telepathic component to it
before or after the experience.

Does that make them schizotypal or just ordinary
people experiencing something our society doesn't yet
consider "real"?

Indulge me for just a moment, but if you can
imagine you had an experience similar to the ones
mentioned in this book, don't you think it might
change your worldview in a big way? In ways that
go beyond the idea of "normal"?

If you think about it, just by the way we've defined
what "schizotypal" means, anyone who's experienced
something beyond our current paradigm's definition
of reality will get slapped with such a diagnosis, even
if they're entirely mentally healthy.

And let's not forget that the definitions of mental
illness change from decade to decade. As recently as
the early 1970's, homosexuality was listed in the psy-
chiatric profession's DSM manual as a mental illness.
Does anyone today seriously think that gay men and

women are inherently mentally ill? Just think how quickly our definitions have changed in that respect.

Secondly, this reporter's comment ignored the reality that many of these witnesses came from government and military jobs with extensive psychological screening and yearly mental fitness reports ("Fit Rep" tests). Do you think our government lets people with schizophrenia be in charge of launching nuclear missiles? I highly doubt it. This diagnosis also includes the characteristic of "works poorly with others," which is not typical of people in high-level government, military, or private industry jobs like airline pilots who have constant contact with others. In this case, the reporter is taking the easy way out, doubting the credibility of the witnesses instead of looking at the veracity of what they're saying.

If we had similar attitudes towards women's suffrage and the civil rights movement in the 1960's the only people voting now would be white males. Sometimes you have to step up to the plate and take a swing at the ball; you can't win the game by bunting.

Essentially, ignoring qualified witnesses either retired from service in the federal government or private industry, people we usually trust our lives to every day to do their jobs, is a type of abuse. It doesn't leave physical scars, but it impairs mental health: ours and that of the witnesses. We can do better than that.

And I would suggest the following: if the witnesses are telling the truth about what they've seen and we refuse to listen to them or take them seriously, isn't society suffering from a schizotypal delusion? Isn't an avoidance of known, natural phenomena a type of mass social delusion or reality distortion?

When I talk about this topic in public, I often get the response that if this issue were real, if there were enough data to support it, it would become self-evident and make its way into the scientific literature, the news, and mass opinion.

While such a response is understandable, it ignores a couple of essential points. First, as we've seen, scientific discoveries can be ignored for a long time. It took about one hundred years, for example, for Antony van Leeuwenhoek, inventor of the microscope, to be accepted by the medical community (Wootton, *Bad Medicine*) because doctors didn't think it added anything to their practice.

The example of meteorites mentioned earlier or Dan Schechtman's quasicrystal discovery also shows that science has its status quo interests to suppress innovation. Schechtman, an Israeli crystal researcher, was thrown out of the Union of Crystallographers after he discovered 5-sided crystals and dismissed by chemist Linus Pauling and others as a "quasi-scientist." Schechtman won the Nobel Prize for his discovery in 2005.

So, just because the scientific mainstream doesn't

accept a particular idea isn't evidence that it's not real.

Secondly, because of the critical national security implications of what seems like waves of sightings and contact with the unknown, unidentifiable aerial craft, the so-called "national security state" can suppress this type of information in many ways. It was decided to do just that by the Robertson Panel in 1953 mainly because of the potential for mass panic, especially during times of warfare. Just take the following example.

The researcher and author Jim Marrs, who wrote the foreword for my first book, *Opening Minds,* tells the following story. He knew someone whose job it was at one of the big three TV networks to collate all the news from local sources throughout the United States on weekends and decide what would be of interest on their nightly weekend national TV news show.

This person had the authority to present any stories he saw as appropriate to the show with two exceptions: terrorism and UFO-related news. He told Marrs that with the first type, terrorism, the story had to go upstairs to get edited, and then it would be sent back down to his show with edits for obvious reasons. However, with the second type of story, UFOs, his rough draft of the story would be sent upstairs, and it never came down again. It was a one-way flow of information. And this news editor was never told why.

This type of de facto censorship can prevent discussion of the subject despite the massive evidence to the contrary.

We have lots of convincing evidence and witness testimony, sworn under oath, from highly credible people about what they've seen and experienced.

Just take the 600 or so witnesses to the Roswell events of 1947, both in New Mexico and Wright-Patterson AFB in Dayton, OH, who either saw the same types of metal materials or bodies of what appeared to be humanoids. (*Witness to Roswell*, Schmidt and Carey).

Or more recently, the thirty or so U.S. military policemen who witnessed the Rendlesham Forest incidents in December 1980, including the radar tower operators. The events over three nights have evidence that includes audiotapes recorded at the time of the incidents, plaster of Paris casts of the imprints left by the craft in the soil, Geiger counter readings, and lots of corroborative testimony.

More witnesses have come forward recently, including the radar operators and other MPs, that corroborate the testimony of the original witnesses. (*The Guardian* Dec. 2016)

It's just not plausible to say it didn't happen.

Then there are the mass sightings in Phoenix, AZ in 1997 and the Hudson Valley sightings in the New

York area in the 1980's whose witnesses included many local and state police officers and even the security guards at the Indian Point Nuclear Reactor. This information is not just hearsay. The Citizen Hearing mentioned earlier had lots of credible testimony given under oath to retired Congressional lawmakers.

The decision to avoid this topic as a society, mainly in the United States, is not a result of a lack of evidence. There's too much evidence. In my assessment, we avoid it because of fear that if we start an honest discussion of the topic, we don't know where it will take us. We fear the unknown and fear the immensity of the universe.

And because we all share that fear, to some degree or another, we're happy to let those who know about it keep quiet. And they're content to do the same.

The German sociologist Georg Simmel observed that secrecy is a form of power and that in modern societies, trust has replaced information. Because there is so much information we can't verify personally and a very specific division of labor, we must trust that the authority figures and everyday people we encounter tell us the truth. We don't have time to verify all the information ourselves.

But in this case, when there's so much evidence and so much official silence, we have to ask if that trust is misplaced.

As sociologists have noted: "with ever-increasing divisions of labor, specialization, and complexity, social life becomes more standardized, controlled and segmented or compartmentalized." (Marx and Muschert 2008)

Perhaps that compartmentalization has gone so far that we're now effectively living in a self-created, mass "reality distortion field."

Chapter Fifteen—Lyn Buchanan and the Extraterrestrial Control Panel

Lyn Buchanan is one of the best-known remote viewers and teachers in the world, having served in the Defense Intelligence Agency remote viewing program, later known as Project Star Gate, starting in 1984. Lyn wasn't one of the two original groups of military people trained by natural psychic Ingo Swan, but he got to know him later on. Lyn was initially chosen for the program for his telekinetic abilities by which he can influence physical objects with his mind. This was demonstrated when he inadvertently shorted out a considerable part of the military's computer networks after someone intentionally sabotaged his database demonstration at a NATO meeting. Lyn's anger, misdirected towards the computer he was using, was later deemed to be the cause of the short circuit that spread throughout the network. This event was recounted briefly in the movie, "The Men Who Stare At Goats."

Seeing some potential for his destructive abilities, General Bert Stubblebine, a strong supporter of the government's remote viewing program, recruited Lyn in the program with the idea of Lyn being able to use his "remote influencing" abilities to destroy and control enemy computer systems.

I've taken two of Lyn's viewing classes at his home in New Mexico and heard him give several presentations at conferences. Here is one of the stories he's told about an abduction experience.

Around 1989, an incident caused Lyn to remember a suppressed abduction experience he had had almost 25 years before that time. At the time of the abduction, he had been moving from one home to another. His wife had already gone to the other home, and he was finishing up at the old one. It was late, so he made a pallet on the floor and lay down. Something landed in the backyard. He tried to get up to see what it was but couldn't move. Beings from the object came around the side of the house, entered, and took him into the object. He was placed with a group of similarly paralyzed people, but they could not keep him paralyzed, so they took him to the control area where they could keep watch on him. He knelt by the pilot, and they talked. He was even allowed to try his hand at the controls for a brief period after the pilot had taught him how to work them.

Almost 25 years later, remembering the event was an overwhelming experience, and Lyn convinced himself that it was just some kind of "false memory syndrome." He tried to ignore it. But he couldn't just put it out of his mind. When he returned to work the Monday after remembering the event, he tasked it to the military remote viewers without letting them know anything about what they would be viewing. Their findings confirmed that his memories were based on fact. One of them reported it up the chain of command, and that week, Lyn was called to the Defense Intelligence Agency. Two men, one a professional interrogator and the other a man from the office that hired the interrogator, took Lyn into a conference room and began to grill him for information. As Lyn answered the interrogator's questions about the UFO's control panel operation, the other man suddenly slapped his leg and said, "So that's it!!" Lyn realized that the man probably had one of the crafts and didn't know how to fly it. This was a second confirmation that the abduction had been real, but Lyn was still skeptical and held onto the idea that it could have all been in his imagination.

Then, the following year, while out on a mission, Lyn met an old Army buddy who offered to show him where he worked: a hanger where experts studied the wreckage of mid-air collisions. While Lyn was shown the wreckage, he saw a piece of debris that looked like the control panel he had been allowed to briefly operate while onboard the spaceship many years before. Without thinking, he blurted out to his friend, "Hey! That's out of a UFO!" Lyn's words echoed through the hanger, and he was soon forcibly "escorted" out of the facility. Seeing that piece was the final confirmation for Lyn that his abduction event had been real.

A recounting of most of the things that happened and what Lyn learned from the pilot while on the "abduction trip" is very lengthy and can be found in Jim Marrs' book, *Alien Agenda*. Readers will also enjoy Lyn's book about his remote viewing experiences *The Seventh Sense*.

Lyn Buchanan

Chapter Sixteen—Woman and Mother See Hudson Valley Triangle

During the early 1980's the Hudson Valley area was the scene of numerous sightings of unexplained, large triangular craft. At least twenty-thousand people saw these craft over the lower New York and Connecticut area from 1982-87. In great detail, these events were written about in Dr. Allen Hynek, Bob Pratt, and Phil Imbrogno's book Night Siege.

In 1985, a woman I know and her mother were walking up a large hill near Inwood Hill Park in Washington Heights, NYC. The woman told me that they suddenly spotted a large triangular craft around seven stories high and about 250 feet across with colored lights around it. She said that many people were looking out their apartment windows at the object, some pointing at it, which appeared low over the ground near the Hudson River. She later had trouble remembering details about the incident and was surprised to learn that there were other sightings in the area around that time.

The Hudson Valley UFO, as it's called, was seen by thousands of people, including many police officers, in Westchester County and neighboring areas. Most sightings occurred at night. Official explanations from the NY State Police and the FAA were that people were seeing Cessna pilots or ultralights flying in formation. However, the object could hover with very little or no sound and then take off rapidly. Witnesses described it as a single, solid, dark structure that blocked out stars.

In fact, one of my crop circle tour participants in 2008, a woman named Pam, while living in Yorktown Heights, NY in the early to mid-1980's, saw a triangular-shaped, completely silent object with red lights pass right over her house. It seemed to be about the size of two school buses in length forming a V-shape with one red light at the front and several on each side. She told me in no uncertain terms that it was totally silent: it was not an ultra-light vehicle or a formation of Cessna's, common explanations told to the public by the FAA or local police when they reported such sightings.

Chapter Seventeen—Dr. Richard Hoover: NASA's Extraterrestrial Fossils; Skylab Photos; Disc Causes Soviet Missile Launch Sequence Initiation

I met Prof. Richard B. Hoover (Astrobiologist at Athens State University and the University of Buckingham) at the 2014 International UFO Congress Conference in Scottsdale, Arizona, presenting his research results about carbon-rich cyanobacteria fossils that he had discovered in carbonaceous meteorites. These discoveries are considered very controversial by some scientists. Hoover is a well-credentialed scientist with over 300 scientific conference proceedings, peer-reviewed papers, and 35 books. Hoover also holds 23 U.S. and international patents and is a recognized world authority on diatoms and microbial "extremophiles": organisms that can survive in deep crustal rocks and the deepest ocean trenches, in hot springs, geysers, glaciers, polar ice caps, and even on spent nuclear reactor fuel rods â€" in short, in the most extreme environmental conditions.

Hoover worked for NASA at the Marshall Space Flight Center in Huntsville, Alabama, where he headed the NASA Marshall Space Flight Center Astrobiology Program from 1997 to 2011. He was awarded the NASA inventor of the year in 1992, and he retired from NASA on Dec. 31, 2011, after almost half a century of service with the agency.

I spent a lot of time talking with Richard at the conference, and he told me some incredible things.

The first evidence for fossilized cyanobacteria and other microbes was found in the Orgueil and Ivuna CI1 carbonaceous meteorites by Nagy, Claus, and Palik in 1962. These results were dismissed as resulting either from pollen contamination or as the result of an intentional hoax. Prof. Hoover followed this debate closely and was skeptical of the contamination claims because the fossils had been found embedded in the rock matrix. He had also discussed this early work with diatomist friends and scientists such as Sir Robert Ross, Fred Hoyle, and Sam Van Landingham, who conducted and confirmed these results in their independent studies. Prof. Hoover and his colleague Academician Alexei Yurivitch Rozanov, Director of the Paleontology Institute of the Russian Academy of Sciences in Moscow, had independently discovered Cyanobacteria fossils in these stones. He informed Richard that the claims that these remains were pollen were ridiculous. After several years of intensive study, both he and Academician Rozanov have never encountered a single pollen grain in interior regions of any meteorites studied. Furthermore, the fossils of Cyanobacteria (phototrophic "blue-green algae " that require light to grow) were millions of years old, and they were embedded inside the interior of jet-black rocks.

Richard told me that he has found, imaged, and analyzed these fossils with X-ray Spectroscopy in many different carbonaceous meteorites. Their lack of nitrogen proves they are ancient and not recent biological contaminants that could have invaded these meteorites after arriving on Earth in the past two centuries. He has concluded that these fossils represent proof of the existence of extraterrestrial life. These discoveries, coupled with meteorites on Earth from comets and Mars and his studies of meteorite micro-fossils and diatoms and other extremophile life forms on Earth (found living everywhere from deep volcanic vents in the ocean floor to the frozen ice of Antarctica) that microbial life must be widely distributed in the universe.

However, the subject of evidence for extraterrestrial life is considered controversial at NASA. This is evidenced by the fact that NASA has not flown a so-called "Single Life Detection Experiment" to Mars since the Viking missions in 1976. Furthermore, the McKay data on possible microfossils in the Mars meteorite ALH 84001 (that triggered the modern Astrobiology Program) were subsequently highly criticized at NASA, as was Hoover's 2011 review paper discussing prior discoveries of microfossils in meteorites that had previously been approved by NASA and published in peer-reviewed scientific articles and books.

His supervisor informed him that officials in The White House were worried that *"a report on extraterrestrial life might be offensive to some of the fundamentalist churches in the US and possibly other religions."*

According to Prof. Hoover, NASA has a timetable for releasing information about water on Mars and the possibility of extraterrestrial life. As evidence of this, he showed the audience pictures of snow on Mars, taken by the NASA Viking landers. Although Viking took this spectacular color image in 1979, NASA did not release the picture until 1997 after the ALH 84001 McKay paper was published. It was released in 1997 in a NASA Poster, "Postcards from Mars," to the public, and at that time, it was added to the archive on the NASA website. Hoover believed that he was the first to present this image in 1998 at a NATO Permafrost Symposium in Novosibirsk Siberia and to publish it as it appeared in his scientific paper in the Volume on the NATO Permafrost Conference.

Skylab incident and subsequent photo cover-up

Hoover also told me that he was on the communications console at NASA, Johnson Space Center, in 1973 when Skylab astronaut Owen Garriott reported to the CAPCOM (the Capsule Commander or person designated by NASA to talk with the astronauts) that they were observing "red lights" outside the Skylab Wardroom window. They were taking photos of this object that appeared to be in orbit with Skylab.

After the Mission, Owen discussed the event at a press conference and said NASA would know more after analyzing the photos and radar data. It was thought that the images would be made public after the film was developed.

Several years later, Richard phoned his friend, Noel Lamar, the NASA JSC photo lab Director, at a colleague's request to request a copy of the red light photos. As the Director was out of his office, another friend answered the phone, the lab worker who had worked closely with Hoover while they selected the films that would be flown on the Skylab S-056 X-Ray telescope. The lab assistant described the red light photos to Hoover, gave him the image frame numbers, and told the person's name at NASA MSCF who had prints of these images. Just then, Noel returned, and the lab assistant transferred the call to him.

When Richard asked the Director for copies of the photos, there was a long silence on the other end of the phone line.

The Director then told him that the pictures â€œdid not come out." He said it had all been a mistake and that the red lights were just a reflection of red panel lights within Skylab and that the lens had been pressed against the window, so the light did not reflect back into the camera and that there was really nothing on the outside of Skylab. Hoover was astonished as it contradicted all he had just been told. He asked Noel how that was possible since the camera was an SLR, and Owen would never have wasted precious film if nothing was there when he looked into the viewfinder.

He then asked the director how NORAD could

have tracked these lights on radar if they were merely reflections in the window. The director said he had heard nothing about radar tracking and asked why Hoover thought that had occurred. When told it was discussed over the "open com loops" in real-time, *Hoover was told his memory must be mistaken,* and the conversation ended with Hoover amazed by these curious discordant conversations with two friends that he trusted and believed to both be completely honest and trustworthy.

Hoover and his colleague went to see the images at the office of the MSFC official that had a book containing "all of the Skylab photos from this camera." They then discovered that photos with the frame numbers of the red light images were missing from the book. That particular sequence of shots was simply absent.

A few years later, Richard was at a science conference in Boulder, Colorado, when he stopped in at a book store. He found a book *UFO's: Past, Present, and Future* based on the documentary by the same name, produced by Robert Emenegger and Allan Sandler at the request of the U.S. Air Force in the mid-1970's.

This documentary was an honest look at the UFO phenomenon initially intended for mass distribution. Emenegger was invited by U.S. Air Force officials to a tour of Holloman AFB and was shown where an actual encounter had taken place between ET's and the Air Force. The Air Force told Emenegger they had been in contact with this ET group for a while. This encounter was depicted in the film, even a few frames of the actual ET craft landing, though not the complete film as originally promised by the Air Force.

Parts of this movie were filmed in the Pentagon and narrated by Air Force officials: they weren't making fun of the subject either. However, a few weeks before it was to appear in movie theaters, the Air Force strangely changed their mind, and the film was never distributed. However, it was released as a TV documentary in 1976 with new commentary by Jaques Vallee as "UFO's: Past, Present, and Future," and you can see it on YouTube today. (It was previously called "UFO's: It Has Begun.") I highly recommend it.

So while leafing through the book, Richard was stunned to see the very photographs he had been told didn't exist, complete with unexplained luminous objects photographed by the Skylab astronauts Owen Garriott and Al Bean.

Hoover's stories above suggest that NASA is engaged in a long-running, large-scale coverup of both microbial and life-size extraterrestrial evidence.

Richard then told me an ever more bizarre and alarming story. Sometime in the 1990's he had been hosting Dr. Muradin A. Kumakhov of the Kurchatov Institute, initially founded in 1943 as the USSR's leading laboratory for developing nuclear weapons.

Kumakhov, a pioneer in Polycapillary X-ray Optics for Astronomy and discoverer of the eponymous Kumakhov radiation, oversaw somewhere in the neighborhood of 65,000 people, including all things nuclear, including power plants and missiles.

Missile launch sequence initiated by flying disc

They were having pickles and Vodka when Kumakhov told him that in the early 1980's a giant flying disc, hundreds of feet across, had come over a Soviet missile installation in the Ukraine (possibly the same incident as occurred in Carpathian Military District near the town of Byelokoroviche on October 4th, 1982). The elliptical object hovered for about fifteen minutes, and then suddenly, many of the missiles entered launch mode, starting their ominous countdown sequence towards zero. The missile operators could do nothing to override this situation, and they panicked. Calls were made to Moscow. This alarming situation lasted until just **thirty seconds** from launch, which would have sent these thermonuclear weapons to their destinations. Then, suddenly, everything went back to normal. After the incident, all the wires between that base and Moscow were pulled out and examined, but they found nothing out of the ordinary.

136

This is not an isolated incident, as seen in other chapters of this book. Similar events happened at American missile bases starting in the 1960's. However, in these cases, the missiles were mainly turned off by the mysterious craft, and in some instances, such as in Minot, N.D., the launch sequences were initiated just as in the Ukraine case.

[Video available for this chapter.]

Richard Hoover and the author

Chapter Eighteen—Pilot's Sighting During Radar Exercise; B-52 Incident over Soviet Border During Cold War

A friend of mine, "Jack," a former airline pilot, both for the military and a commercial airline, related these stories to me.

In 1964, Jack was in the Air Force flying radar calibration flights in North Dakota for NORAD to ensure the radar was working correctly. One morning he was flying a typical triangular route in an F-101B with 200 miles between each point on the path. He was in the back seat operating as the Radar Intercept Officer.

These were daily flights very early in the morning.

On this day, there was a layer of clouds at 20,000 feet below them and another layer above them at about 30,000 feet.

Suddenly, he and the pilot noticed a dark gold-colored, football-shaped object flying about 4,000 feet below them in the opposite direction. It could have been as large as a civilian wide-body aircraft. He and the pilot saw it for about one minute in total. It did not appear on their radar, and because of the importance of the mission they were flying, there should not have been any other air traffic in their vicinity.

Because of mission security, they did not communicate with their military control tower unless necessary. However, Jack suggested to the pilot in the front that they turn around and follow it. The pilot, however, did not want to deviate from their mission, so they never found out what it was.

Unidentified crafts from space disrupt B-52 convoy during Six-Day War

Jack's second story was even more dramatic. He said he was flying on a domestic flight one-day from the U.S., and nothing particular was going on, and he told his co-pilot about the above incident from 1964. The co-pilot then told Jack about his riveting account of an experience from several decades before.

The co-pilot said he was piloting a B-52 over Turkey near the U.S.S.R border in 1967. It was during the 6-day war between Israel and the Arab states. The United States wanted to send a strong message to the Soviets not to get involved. The B-52's were nuclear-armed and flew around the clock in convoys of three planes along the U.S.S.R border. They refueled in flight from KC-135 tankers. The pilot was in the lead plane with two behind him, spaced out at one mile of airspace per plane cruising at 30,000 - 40,000 feet. (This was similar to operation *Chrome Dome* which flew convoys of B-52's, in groups of three, along the Soviet border in different locations throughout the Cold War beginning in the early 1960's.)

Suddenly, a group of three objects came down from the right at about a 45-degree angle and positioned themselves in a "fingertip formation," which is like a V shape, in front of the lead plane that this pilot was flying. They then went around the wing tip on the left side of the aircraft and started moving to the rear of the convoy. The electronics and radio operator then told the pilot, "Sir, we're being scanned on all frequencies."

The unidentified objects moved to the tail of the rear-most plane and then came up along the right side of the convoy. They then were in front of the lead plane again. The objects did this three times. The pilot told Jack they could tell these were physical objects because they could feel the wake left by the objects as their B-52 passed through the same airspace. The objects were close enough that the pilot could take a picture of them with a new Nikon camera that his wife had given him the previous Christmas. The things then left the way they had come, moving away exceptionally quickly at a 45-degree angle up to the right into the sky.

The pilot radioed in what had happened to his controller. When his plane landed a few days later at an Air Force base in the United States, he was met by men in suits who escorted him and his crew to a special room. They asked for his film and camera. He gave them the camera with the film still in it. The men then said: **"You are NEVER to talk about this again."** The film and Nikon camera were never returned. He was furious about this, given that the camera was a Christmas gift from his wife, and it still bothered him enough decades later to tell Jack about it.

Chapter Nineteen— Aerospace Engineer is Asked to Reverse Engineer Unidentified Nanomaterials

Phil is someone I've known for about two decades in Colorado. He's worked at JPL in Pasadena and Ball Aerospace in Boulder, and a few other defense and aerospace companies. I was talking to him at a science meeting one day, and he told me the following story.

His superiors at an aerospace company came to his group and told them they had some materials that they didn't understand. They told Phil's group to see if they could figure out how it worked. They said to Phil's group: "The people who made it went away." Phil said that everyone in the group looked at the materials and concluded from their sheer complexity that they had to be extraterrestrial in origin.

142

So I asked Phil: "So you thought they were extraterrestrial?"

Phil replied with total certainty: "*No, I know they were extraterrestrial.*"

I recently saw Phil again in 2016 at the Society for Scientific Exploration meeting, and he reaffirmed the story.

Chapter Twenty—Jan: Father Flew Roswell Wreckage to Wright Field

I was sitting in a Kosher Deli in Boulder, Colorado. An informal talent show was about to begin, and a sign-up sheet was being passed around for people who wanted to perform a skit or musical act. A woman next to me passed me the sheet, and I asked her if she was going to do something for the show. Her response was: *"Have you ever heard about Roswell?"*

I've never started a conversation this way before, but it just so happened that I had heard a lecture about the Roswell Crash of 1947 just a few days earlier, by author Jim Marrs, near Greeley, Colorado. It was the first time I had ever learned anything about the incident. Marrs presented the case that what crashed was not a weather or military balloon but something much more extraordinary: a claim supported by many other authors and researchers and over 600 witnesses but still denied by the Air Force.

So I told Jan about hearing the Jim Marrs lecture and how I had never heard much about it before. Jan then proceeded to tell me that her father had been a pilot for the 509th bomb group and had been kept on after World War II to fly missions over East Asia. Two weeks before he died, he had called each of his four daughters individually into his hospital room. He told them that he had flown wreckage from the Roswell crash in a circuitous route through Texas to what is today known as Wright-Patterson Air Base in Ohio (at the time, it was called Wright Field). He said it had to be something exceedingly important as large wooden crates full of material were guarded by an armed guard with a sidearm on his leg throughout the entire trip. As the flight stopped in Fort-Worth first, the guard never left the crates except to use the bathroom. The pilots of the plane were never allowed near the crates.

Jan was of the personal opinion that the wreckage was from an exceedingly special vehicle. Everything her father told her was consistent with what she had read in Philip Corso's book, *The Day After Roswell*. He told her he had been afraid to talk about it before for fear that something would happen to his family in retaliation.

I asked Jan if she could be a guest on my radio

show which I was hosting at the time, and she said it might be possible, but she would have to think about it, not wanting to cause any distress to her sisters about going public with her father's story. I attempted to follow up with Jan, but she never returned my emails. It turns out that I wasn't the only one to talk with Jan. Don Schmidt, the co-author of *Witness to Roswell: Unmasking the Government's Biggest Cover-up* and *Inside The Real Area 51: The Secret History of Wright Patterson,* when I asked him once about whether he had met Jan, confirmed that he had. She had told him the same story. She had come to the Roswell Museum in New Mexico while he happened to be there. He had found her to be very credible because of the precise detail her father had relayed to her. Don had lost track of her also and thought her story to be of high importance as only a few pilots flew Roswell wreckage out of the base and over to Wright-Patterson.

There are plenty of good books written about the Roswell incident, and readers are encouraged to do their research. I'll say that the highest-ranking official ever to comment about Roswell was Brigadier General Thomas Dubose, who spoke about the event on camera in 1991. Dubose was an assistant to deputy commander of Strategic Air Command at the Pentagon, General Clements McMullen, in charge of the Roswell event. Dubose is on record as saying that the

146

official Army story about the wreckage being from a balloon was a cover story designed for the public. His boss McMullen said to him: **"This is more than Top Secret, it's beyond that. This is of the highest priority, and you are never to say anything about it."**

Brigadier General Thomas Dubose, assistant to General Clements McMullan, Deputy Commander of Strategic Air Command

And another high-ranking official, General Arthur Exon, who served at Wright Field in 1947 and later was its Base Commander in the 1960's is on record as saying:

"They knew they had something new in their hands. The metal and material were unknown to anyone I talked to . . . Everyone from the White House on down knew that what we had found was not of this world within 24 hours of our finding it . . . Roswell was the recovery of a craft from space."

Brigadier General Arthur Exon, Wright-Patterson Air Force Base Commander

Chapter Twenty-One—John: Daylight Sighting of Bronze Disc; Attempted Shoot Down of "Off-World Craft" Over Lake Superior

In 1997, shortly after I started teaching remote viewing in Boulder, CO, I met a man we'll call "John," from Northern Colorado who was interested. He took all three levels of my Resonant Viewing classes in Boulder.

Sometimes you think you know someone well. But it wasn't until almost twenty years after I met John that he shared the following two stories with me.

He said he was driving with his father in the early

1970's up by an 11-mile reservoir near Woodland Park, Colorado, to go fishing. His dad had been in the Air Force. He was a navigator and a top-gunner for a B-25 Mitchell Marauder during WW2 and a co-pilot for a Convair B-36 bomber during the Korean War. He was also a base commander at Finland Air Force base on Lake Superior in Northern Michigan.

He was currently serving in Aerospace Defense Command in Colorado Springs, which was created in 1968 and subsumed by NORAD in 1980, the organization that is responsible for maintaining airspace security over the United States and Canada.

As they drove up the mountains to get to the reservoir, they saw a bronze disc, about 50 to 100 feet across just above the ground, moving swiftly over hills. It came right over their truck at about 100 feet, and both vehicle windows were open. John could hear a whooshing sound as it went by overhead.

The truck lurched as if misfiring, and the radio made static-like sounds as the disc went over the vehicle.

John's dad said: "*What the fuck was that?*"

John said his father knew every plane in the U.S. military and could identify them by the sound of their engines alone. Yet, he couldn't identify what he had just seen. They both watched the disc move out of sight over the nearest hill.

When they got to their boat at the reservoir, John

said his dad started drinking five to seven shots of
hard alcohol, apparently due to the stress of the encounter. Under normal circumstances, they would
have stayed all day into the evening when the fishing
gets better as the fish come closer to the surface
because of low light.

However, they only stayed an hour and turned
around to go back home in this case. His father had
a troubled look on his face: while he was on the lake
and during the drive back to Colorado Springs.

As they were driving back, John asked his dad
about what they had seen. John was amazed by it.
John said that his dad then unexpectedly hit him with
the back of his hand and said: "*You are never, EVER to
say a fucking word about what we saw today to anyone.
UNDERSTAND, BOY?*"

As soon as they got back home, his dad put on his
Air Force uniform, made a call on the phone, and said,
to whoever was on the other end: "*There's been an
incident.*" He was then gone for several days.

Incident over Lake Superior

John also recalls an earlier incident that happened in
1964 over Lake Superior. Before moving to Peterson
Air Force Base in Colorado, John told me that his
father, who had a Plus-P security clearance (above

that of the President of the United States), worked as a major at Finland Air Base in Minnesota. John was able to hear his father talking late at night in hushed tones with other officers through the air vents in his room. He would then sneak down the stairs to listen in to the conversation.

John said that one night in 1972, when he was in sixth grade, he heard about the following incident. His father was talking about an "OWC" or "Off-World Craft," as they were referred to in his father's unit.

A craft had come in from outer space and was being tracked by Canadian Central Air Command, who attempted to communicate with it. The Canadians followed the flying object from behind as it traveled at about 1,000 mph. They then radioed ahead to the American Air Defense command what was transpiring.

The craft then crossed over into Minnesota, where the Air Force at Finland Air Base attempted to communicate with it, but to no avail. Two F-106 Star Fighters tried to intercept and communicate with the craft as it came over American air space. John's father, who had the rank of Major, ordered the jet fighters to each launch two missiles at the craft. It was somewhere between midnight and 2 A.M. The craft was never visually seen by the pilots but was identified by radar.

The jet pilots then radioed back that the missiles had failed to reach their targets, their jet engines had flamed out, and they were going into Lake Superior. Their planes disappeared from Finland Air Base radar, and the OWC took off at high speed.

That was the last transmission ever received from the pilots.

Later on, the planes were discovered at the bottom of Lake Superior with their canopies intact. A Navy salvage operation recovered the aircraft from the lake bottom, but there were no traces of the pilots, flight suits, or helmets.

John later met another person many few years later, "Bob," who was stationed at Finland Air Force base and was familiar with this incident. He told John that he was on duty that night and morning. Bob said that as the F-106's closed in on the UFO, they disappeared from the radar screen. The UFO then took off and was gone in two radar sweeps. John asked Bob how the fast that would have been: he was told that would have been from 1,000 mph to 6,000 mph and then to 8,000 mph, somewhere around Mach ten. This would create g-forces on any craft occupants that no humans could withstand.

Bob also said that before he got off duty that morning, government agents in suits and dark glasses took all the information and records from the radar station and interrogated people. *The government agents intimidated people and threatened to throw anyone in jail who talked about the incident.*

154

Readers should note a similar incident involving an F-89 fighter jet from Kinross Air Base over Lake Superior in 1953. Apparently, in this case, the blips from the unknown object and the F-89 merged into one, and the fighter jet was never seen again.

Chapter Twenty-Two—Teri: Aerial Object Leaves Burn Marks on Ground; Kindergarten "Secret School"

Teri is someone I've known for almost two decades since she attended some of my remote viewing classes in 1998. Over the years, she's mentioned some of the following stories in her childhood.

Teri was sleeping out in the backyard with two friends in 1977 in Kaysville, UT. They were lying there looking at the stars, Teri was starting to wake up feeling groggy, and there was a craft above so big she couldn't see the end of it, made of really dark metal, moving very slowly, with lots of pipes, jagged edges, things hanging down. Her friend Lisa was looking at it, and suddenly a light came zipping by. There was complete silence, and even the ship was silent. The ship was moving due North away from them. They felt like they were in a trance. They woke up completely as it was over them; they couldn't wake up their friend Linda who never wanted to talk about it again.

A few weeks later, a friend had a birthday party; she lived across the street, and behind her was a hollow with meadows and trees and livestock. They were sleeping out, they had invited some boys over, and suddenly they saw this "thing" come down, it was round, its lights spinning around the outside edge, red and blue, and orange and white. It made a "whoop whoop" sound as it descended. It was around 45 feet in diameter, a dome shape on top and bottom. The kids all freaked out; it hovered for a while over the trees and then moved into the trees. The kids all ran into the house and told the Dad. He came out and was looking but didn't see anything. But he said they had to sleep inside. The next day Teri told her brother about it, and they went over to the hollow, and they found a perfectly round burnt spot and a tree stump that was also burn't, the same size as the craft the night before. Within the charred surface, all the grasses were charred. They told Lisa's Dad, and he didn't believe them. The burnt spot was there for quite a while, but no adults ever went to look.

Secret school

When Teri was a kid, they put her in kindergarten. She remembers going into the bushes near the school and sitting there. She would be at a school inside a craft, and she would move a ball with her hand inside a grid, and they would show Teri this green, pristine planet, and then all of sudden it would be polluted, burn't and brown, and it didn't feel good. Teri told me she thought they were telepathically giving her information about the importance of taking care of the Earth and about how it was our choice to do so or not.

There were other kids there. They each had a grid to play with. One of the creatures looked like a giant praying mantis, and others were short with big eyes with skin-tight suits. Then they would bring Teri back to the bushes.

Teri would go home and tell her mom how much she liked school, and she would sing songs she had learned while on the craft.

Eventually, the school called and asked Teri's mom why she hadn't been going to school! She had been absent for two weeks.

Teri remembers that they had to make a paper mache model, and she constructed a perfect model of Jupiter, then made a spaceman out of contact paper.

Chapter Twenty-Three—Betsy and the Flying Disc with Military Jets in Pursuit

A friend of mine, Betsy, was taking a Chi Gong course near Cottonwood, Arizona. One morning, she was up early practicing up in the cliffs with a group of fellow practitioners when she noticed a bright light in the sky. Her instructors told her and the rest of the group to turn around and practice in another direction. Everyone complied except Betsy. She focused her practice on what she thought was a star for the next 15 minutes. The other stars disappeared as the sun came up, but the 'star' Betsy saw remained big and bright.

After about 10 minutes, the bright object rotated clockwise and turned into a gray, disc-shaped object about three times bigger than the bright light. It remained stationary for about five minutes until Betsy saw what appeared to be fighter jets racing towards it.

The disc slowly rotated counter-clockwise as the jets got closer and then shot off at lightning speed into space. The fighter jets broke formation, turned around, and flew off in the opposite direction.

[Video available for this chapter.]

Chapter Twenty-Four—The Price of Silence

Among the witnesses I've encountered, there is lots of fear in talking about this subject, particularly those who've held federal security clearances. They've expressed fear of losing their pensions, retirement benefits and concern over their families' safety. And sometimes they don't know what they've seen; what type of life form did they encounter?

And if you think about all the stress, this causes it has to add up both emotionally and economically. In many cases, the price of silence is a shutting down of some part of these witnesses' emotional and intellectual systems because they always wonder what they saw. Still, they can't explore it any further. So they've just shut down in some ways.

It takes a lot of courage to explore the unknown. It's a lot easier to go with the status quo. Explorers of all types have always faced a lot of ridicule. But if it weren't for these interested, curious, and bold people who discovered new lands and ideas, we'd be living in a very different world today.

Apple used to have a TV ad that started with "Here's to the crazy ones." It celebrated all the positive attributes of independent thinkers, innovators, and inventors. You have to be a little bit crazy sometimes to venture into the unknown, where you can be ridiculed and ostracized by the rest of society.

It's helpful to remember that people accused the Wright Brothers when they were doing early tests of their Flyer at Kitty Hawk of being just two "poor, lonely nuts." Perhaps to avoid public ridicule, they chose a beekeeper and publisher named Amos Root, rather than mainstream media, to write about their early flights outside Dayton, Ohio. (McCullough, 2016).

As writer Dorothea Brand is reported to have said: "The Wright brothers flew through the smokescreen of impossibility."

This subject area may seem impossible to investigate or understand, but someone has to do it. The cost of keeping this matter secret is that the secrecy spreads: It then creates more secrecy. And Democratic Republics don't do well with secretiveness. If we continue to keep this topic secret, how many other secrets are out there? How many more witnesses? How many other organizations about which the public knows far too little? It's the worst kind of political and moral "slippery slope."

A well-known Latin saying is, "Who is guarding

the guards?" (Quis custodiet ipsos custodes?) In this case, possibly no one.

And on the other side, what are the costs to people's mental health, those of the witnesses and their families who would like to tell us what they know but don't. Some argue that it might threaten national security if we knew the truth about what's going on. But national security is more than just having vigorously defended borders: it's also the integrity of our national infrastructure, including its citizens' mental integrity. And holding back vital information about the reality we live in is potentially a massive threat to our mental and social integrity.

In the 1950's President Eisenhower pushed for all sorts of defense authorization bills. The National Defense Transportation Act built uniform, national highways; the National Defense Education Act funded scholarships for college students in particular disciplines to improve the nation's security in the wake of Soviet advancements in space technology. He realized that national security is about much more than a well-armed and prepared military: security involves every aspect of our day-to-day existence.

The overwhelming government secrecy we live with today is the product of World War II and the Cold War that followed, including thermonuclear weapons production and the associated bureaucracies that maintained this vast weapons arsenal. And today, there are eighteen different intelligence agencies in the United States federal government, each with separate security classification protocols.

As former missile launch officer and author Robert Salas points out in *UFOs: Unidentified*, during times of war, secrecy takes precedence over openness and transparency for national security reasons. And it's completely understandable.

My father landed on Omaha Beach with the U.S. First Infantry during D-Day, June 6, 1944. He was stationed in the Dorset area of the U.K. I've looked through the letters he sent his parents back in New York, and military censors blacked out every mention he made of nearby locations or places. He wasn't even told in the slightest when the invasion would begin, likewise with his letters from Normandy and for the rest of the war.

However, as Salas articulates, secrecy is the enemy of openness, and the paradox is that secrecy is invoked to protect an open society. But you can't have both at the same time. Secrecy is supposed to be a temporary state of affairs during periods of military conflict. There is a cost to having too much secrecy, especially in science and the general skill levels of the population. The secrecy grows.

As Salas states: "Although an official faces disciplinary action for the failure to classify information that should be secret, no instance has been found of an official facing disciplinary or criminal action for classifying material that should have been made public. Therefore, the tendency to 'play it safe' and use the secrecy stamp has been virtually the norm."

As historian and author Richard Dolan points out regarding this subject, secrecy breeds more secrecy. There isn't anyone to stop it. The individuals and organizations that create secrecy have ulterior motives beyond immediate national security to maintain this secrecy, especially when funding their secret "black budget" or "special access" programs.

Secrecy becomes a structure in itself that is its *raison d'etre* (reason for being): it's self-justifying and self-perpetuating. It tends to sustain itself for no externally justifiable reason. It becomes a self-aggrandizing structure ensconced in ever more complex layers of bureaucracy and funding, precisely as the German sociologist Max Weber suggested it would be a century ago.

And so here we are, seventy years after the end of World War II, twenty-five years after the fall of the Soviet Union, and we don't know the complete story about our recent history. Eisenhower's warnings about the dangers of the "military-industrial complex" seem as prescient as ever.

The silence and lack of discussion of critical issues facing our society, like the encounters of people in this book with unknown craft and their occupants, enhances the ultimate dislocating potential and sheer devastating shock effect of the next Black Swan event.

It's a total paradox that we're creating this future event right now by refusing to talk about it!

If a large section of our history has been censored since the late 1940's, allegedly in the name of national security, how secure are we? Isn't the point of an open society to be able to have intelligent discussions and debates about complex and possibly tricky subjects? And if we don't have an open society anymore, what exactly are we defending? The status quo of denying the public the facts on arguably the most crucial development in human history?

We talked in an earlier chapter about Black Swans and their tendency to take everyone by surprise, as the credit crisis of 2008 when national banks had to be propped up by their governments. Aren't we creating the ultimate Black Swan event by maintaining the silence around this critical and mysterious topic?

If you think about it, what could be more undermining to national security than keeping the general public uninformed, misinformed, and misled for over fifty years about perhaps the most enigmatic, perplexing, and quintessential issue of all time?

For example, if you were a resident of Nazi Germany during the 1930's and 40's and lived near a concentration camp, it would be more convenient to say you didn't know what was going on, even if you did. And when the whole neighborhood adopts this attitude, the secrecy becomes self-justifying and permanent. The entire society turns its head away from what's going on. When you smelled the smoke of burning human carcasses, you'd have to wonder what was going on in those buildings at the edge of town. But you wouldn't act because everyone else around you had also accepted it. It becomes a hidden structure protecting you from having to confront Black Swan events. You wouldn't even have to say you were "just following orders" because you've walled yourself off from the truth.

Opening Pandora's Box

The question of why we don't talk about this subject more often is frequently asked by researchers. The usual response is that "if the reality of these phenomena were acknowledged, it would cause the public to panic." While that might be true, or might have been true in the past, I think there's a deeper reason. It seems to me that this topic is like Pandora's Box, both ideologically and legally. Recognizing that there's someone else here on or near our planet and that it's been kept hidden for so many years would raise so many questions that our reality would be bound to change in a big way. And it's doubtful that any of the major institutions and organizations in our society want this to happen. It's unlikely that even most Americans would like that to happen. It's hard to imagine a more significant issue than this.

Because what it suggests is that we don't know the universe we're living in, that we've been like children the whole time, imagining that we're the most evolved, intelligent beings on the planet. And to me, this is perhaps the biggest reason that the secret persists. It's because collectively, it would shake our paradigms of reality to their core.

It doesn't come down to the government or some aerospace company hiding alien bodies or remains of crashed craft. We want our government to protect us from the truth and keep the facade going: to maintain the illusion of our moral superiority over all the other species around us. Because if there were a full Disclosure about this issue, whatever that entails, it would be the immediate end of that illusion. And that's too much for us to absorb or even start thinking about collectively. It would launch us into the **Unknown** in a big way. You can imagine the sense of uncertainty this would create.

In time, all secrets become known. It's the nature of historical evolution. However, in this case, we don't know if it will come out with a "bang" or through a long series of revelations and disclosures of new facts. But either way, we're in for a massive paradigm shift that will dwarf all the other changes we're currently preoccupied with, such as self-driving cars, so-called "artificial intelligence" (AI), and global warming. Unveiling this secret would lead us to question everything we know about the universe. And we can only guess where that would lead.

Cultural Lag and Future Shock

The American sociologist William Fielding Ogburn coined the term "cultural lag" to refer to the shock societies experience when technology changes very rapidly. For example, you could imagine the change in social space and time when automobiles replaced horses or the rapid industrialization that Germany experienced in the late 1800's. The society's culture then has to catch up to the technology.

It's similar to futurist Alvin Toffler's "Future Shock," where things change so quickly we suddenly wake up in an unfamiliar world. And the pace of change accelerates so much that people feel socially displaced. It's a situation that affects previously remote indigenous societies that come into immediate contact with modern ones, such as what happens from time to time to small tribes previously isolated in the Brazilian Amazon rainforest, for example.

The indigenous peoples in these situations can become disoriented, lose their native language, and suffer ill health from declining nutrition or psychological stress.

I'm convinced that unless we come to grips with the topic being discussed here in this book, we're likely to, in some ways, suffer a similar fate.

Chapter Twenty-Five—Our Multidimensional Universe

In the late 1950's, a graduate student in physics at Princeton University, Hugh Everett III, developed an alternative version of quantum mechanics that allowed for the existence of parallel realities or "Many Worlds," as some later named it. Everett was bothered by the idea that there had to be a human observer, as the Copenhagen school of physics maintained, for formal quantum mechanics to make sense. He thus created the idea of a "Universal Wave Function" in which each observation sends the observer into a new parallel reality, every microsecond. Everett suggested there is no wave collapse as John von Neumann and Werner Heisenberg had proposed. According to the idea of "psycho-physical parallelism," all the possibilities are equally real. And all possibilities are actual concrete realities with observers including other versions of you experiencing them.

Instead, Everett based his model on the idea that each of us "split" every moment to fill the spontaneously created multitudes of realities that arise from each nanosecond. All the possible realities are real, and there's a version of you in each of them.

While Everett's model did not allow for the interaction of these parallel worlds, new models do: one, in particular, is called the "Many Interacting Worlds" model. Howard Wiseman, one of the authors of the Many Interacting Worlds idea, has said: "*While our theory doesn't specifically talk about it, the idea of [human] interaction with other worlds can no longer be ruled out.*" That's a significant sentence coming from a physicist and opens the doors for many previously "paranormal" phenomena becoming normalized.

When Everett developed his model, it was so controversial that his thesis advisor, John Wheeler, made him edit it thoroughly so as not to offend the rest of the physics community, especially Niels Bohr of the Copenhagen school. Entire chapters were removed. All references to splitting timelines, parallel worlds, and realities were removed from his dissertation (there are two references to the idea of splitting in a footnote but only referencing responses from the dissertation's proofreaders). Instead, it became a treatise on the "Universal Wave Function," as Everett called it, and then retitled as the "Relative States Formulation of Quantum Mechanics." Bryce Dewitt and his wife later edited it in the 1970's, reinserted the original chapters, and republished the work as the "Many Worlds Interpretation of Quantum Mechanics." Parallel realities have long been the stuff of science fiction, but now, it's become a hot physics topic. Physicists like Max Tegmark of MIT have written entire books about how parallel realities can exist (*Our Mathematical Universe: My Quest for the Ultimate Nature of Reality*). Regardless of which multiverse theory you prefer, the upshot is the same: we live in a multiverse of an infinite or a nearly endless number of parallel realities with parallel Earths and parallel versions of ourselves.

While this may seem mind-boggling or too complicated, in some ways, it's simpler because, in an infinite universe, there's plenty of room for extraterrestrials, intraterrestrials, and just about anything else you can imagine. The paranormal suddenly ceases to be "para" anything; it's just . . . normal. And what we call UFOs could be seen as quite ordinary in a multiverse. So potentially could ghosts, Bigfoot, ESP, and Remote Viewing.

I consider this to be highly significant because a big objection to the subject of extraterrestrials on Earth is that they would have to come from very, very far away in our universe. But what if they are not coming from physically far away at all, but just another region of the multiverse, perhaps another version of our Earth?

When you consider the possibility of subtle interaction or "bleed-through" from alternative realities, as the Many Interacting Worlds theory suggests, so-called "paranormal" phenomena seem somewhat more intelligible. In fact, the astronomer and Air Force Blue Book official J. Allen Hynek proposed the so-called EDI hypothesis, "Extra-Dimensional Intelligence," in addition to the idea of extraterrestrials (ETI), back in the 1970's after working on the project.

It's time to consider that our universe is both more simple and complex than we've imagined and that our imagination is more vital than previously thought.

Chapter Twenty-Six—You Can Hear a Pin Drop

If you look at all the cases described in this book and assume that these are real cases, not spuriously invented by the people telling them, you have to look at these anecdotes as scientific evidence. Such testimony given under sworn oath as it was at the Citizen Hearing is even more vital. It shows that other forms of intelligence surround us though we don't have a good way of conceptualizing them: We haven't yet developed a vocabulary for such phenomena.

You could deny it exists at all, but then you might be in the same boat as Rene Descartes, Isaac Newton, and the French Academy of Sciences in the Seventeen Hundreds who denied the existence of meteorites because "obviously there are no stones in the sky" as mentioned earlier in this book.

Whether you think these are extraterrestrials, ultraterrestrials, or intraterrestrials, the stories presented here and countless others of similar provenance are evidence of *something*.

So do we talk about it as a whole society or not?

So far, we're choosing the latter. And that should make you suspicious that there's more to our universe than you think, much more, and that someone or some group benefits from your ignorance.

At the time of the writing of this book, except a few comments in 2016 by candidate Hillary Clinton, it's just quiet out there on this topic. Nothing! Well, almost nothing. It's not for lack of evidence, as we've seen. Is it because of our self-cowardice and fear of the unknown? At this point, we have more to lose as a society from remaining silent than if we engage the topic with complete discussion, investigations, and hearings, if necessary.

There's a lot of speculation about the potential effects of Disclosure. These mainly focus on negative, adverse, fear-based outcomes that would cause mass panic and possibly cause people to lock themselves in their apartments and homes. However, I think there would also be an equally positive effect that would increase peoples' curiosity and sense of wonder about our universe. And that could be a good thing.

Hundreds of years ago, the Roman Inquisition burned Giordano Bruno at the stake for what they considered to be heretical religious ideas. He also suggested that the universe was infinite and that there might be people and animals living on other planets. It's looking more and more like he was right. Every day it seems, NASA finds new exoplanets in other star systems, many of them similar to Earth. It's only a matter of time before substantive proof for some form of extraterrestrial life arises, be it bacterial or otherwise. It's just a question of when this is going to happen. And let's listen to people like astrobiologist Richard Hoover from a previous chapter in this book. It's already happened with all the bacterial fossils found in carbonaceous meteorites, like the Murchison and Orgalea specimens.

It's not just the federal government withholding secrets about this issue. The public wants it this way, or they would be demanding more information. Yes, the federal government has black budget programs around this issue. However, the public seems to trust that the government knows what it's doing, or they would demand more. They could easily pick up the phone and call their Senator or Congressperson. But they don't.

They don't because it's easier not to know. The public wants to keep ignoring the elephant in the room and then blame the government for the secrecy rather than take responsibility. It's much easier to pretend that you can't do anything about it.

But the point is that we can do a lot at this stage in our history. There are plenty of good-quality YouTube videos with credible witnesses, many online podcasts, and other resources. Every day, people like you or me have never had this many resources available to us before, so it's really up to us to explore all the information at our disposal, have lots of discussions, and make up our minds about this complex subject.

Silence is no longer a viable option.

Website

Thanks for taking the time to read Black Swan Ghosts. I appreciate your patience, persistence, and effort to understand this perplexing topic. You can find witness video and audio interviews and much more at BlackSwanGhosts.com. You can also visit my blog at NewCrystalMind.com.

Bibliography

~~~

Abbot, Edwin. A. 1984. *Flatland: A Romance of Many Dimensions.* New York: New American Library.

Andrews, Colin and Synthia. 2013. *On the Edge of Reality: Hidden Technology, Powers of the Mind, Quantum Physics, Paranormal Phenomena, Orbs, UFOs, Harmonic Transmissions, and Crop Circles.* The Career Press, Inc. Pompton Plains, NJ.

Bockris, John O'M. 2013 *The New Paradigm: A Confrontation Between Physics and The Paranormal Phenomena.* D&M Enterprises Publisher, Texas.

Brown, Courtney. 1996. *Cosmic Voyage: A Scientific Discovery of Extraterrestrials Visiting Earth.* Dutton.

Buchanan, Lyn. 2003. *The Seventh Sense: The Secrets of Remote Viewing as Told By a "Psychic Spy" For the U.S. Military.* Paraview Pocket Books, New York.

Byrne, Peter. 2010. *The Many Worlds of Hugh Everett III: Multiple Universes, Mutual Assured Destruction, and the Meltdown of a Nuclear Family.* Oxford University Press, New York.

Cameron, Grant and T. Scott Crain, Jr. 2013. *UFOs, Area 51 and Government Informants: A Report on Government Involvement in UFO Crash Retrievals.*

182

Keyhole Publishing Company. Rochester. NY.

Carey, Thomas J. and Donald R. Schmitt. 2013. *Inside the The Real Area 51: The Secret History of Wright-Patterson*. New Page Books, Pompton Plains, NJ.

_____. 2007. *Witness to Roswell: Unmasking the 60-year Cover-Up* The Career Press, Inc., Franklin Lake, NJ

Chaitin, Gregory. 2006. *Metamath!: the Quest for Omega*. Vintage Books, NY.

Corso, Philip J. 1998. *The Day After Roswell* Pocket Books.

Dolan, Richard M. 2014. *UFOs for the Twentieth Century Mind* . Richard Dolan Press. Rochester, NY.

_____. 2012. *After Disclosure: When the Government Finally Reveals the Truth About Alien Contact*. New Page Books. 1601632223

_____. 2009. *UFOs and the National Security State: The Cover-Up Exposed, 1973-1991* Keyhole Publishing.

_____. 2002. *UFOs and the National Security State: Chronology of a Coverup, 1941-1973* Hampton Roads Publishing.

Dewitt, Bryce S. and Neil Graham. 1973. "The Many Worlds Interpretation of Quantum Mechanics."

Emenegger, Robert. 1974. *UFO's: Past Present & Future*. Ballantine Books, New York

Friedman, Stanton T. and Kathleen Marden. 2016.

Fact, Fiction, and Flying Saucers: The Truth Behind the Misinformation, Distortion, and Derision by Debunkers, Government Agencies, and Conspiracy Conmen. New Page Books, Pompton Plains, NJ.

_____. 2010 *Science was Wrong: Startling Truths About Cures, Theories, and Inventions "They" Declared Impossible.* New Page Books.

Good, Timothy. *Earth: An Alien Enterprise. The Shocking Truth Behind the Greatest Cover-Up in Human History.* Pegasus Books, New York.

_____. 1989. *Above Top Secret: The Worldwide U.F.O. Cover-Up.* Quill.

Hastings, Robert. 2008. *UFOs and Nukes: Extraordinary Encounters at Nuclear Weapons Sites.* Author House.

Hein, Simeon. 2002. *Opening Minds: A Journey of Extraordinary Encounters, Crop Circles, and Resonance.* Mount Baldy Press, Inc. Boulder, CO.

Hynek, J. Allen, Phil Imbrogno, Bob Pratt. 1998. *Night Siege: The Hudson Valley UFO Sightings.* Llewellyn Publications. St. Paul, MN.

Keel, John. 1975. *The Mothman Prophecies.* Panther Books.

Maccabee, Bruce. 2014. *The FBI-CIA-UFO Connection: Government UFO Secrets Revealed at Last!* Richard Dolan Press, Rochester, New York.

Marrs, Jim. 2007. *Psi Spies: The True Story of America's Psychic Warfare Program.* Career Press.

_____. 1997. *Alien Agenda: Investigating the Extraterrestrial Presence Among Us.* HarperCollins

Marx, Gart T. and Glenn W. Muschert. 2008. "Simmel on Secrecy. A Legacy and Inheritance for the Sociology of Information." *The Possibility of Sociology: 100 Years of Georg Simmel's Investigations into the Forms of Social Organization,* Christian Papiloud and Cécile Rol (eds). Wiesbaden, Germany: VS Verlag für Sozialwissenschaften

May, Edwin C. and Victor Rubel. 2016. *ESP Wars: East and West.* Crossroad Press.

McCullough, David. 2015. *The Wright Brothers.* Simon and Schuster, New York.

Musser, George. 2016. *Spooky Action at a Distance:The Phenomenon That Reimagines Space and Time–and What It Means for Black Holes, the Big Bang, and Theories of Everything.* Scientific American.

Radin, Dean. 2013. *Supernormal: Science, Yoga, and the Evidence for Extraordinary Psychic Abilities.* Deepak Chopra Press.

_____. 2006. *Entangled Minds: Extraordinary Experiences in a Quantum Reality.* Paraview Pocket Books.

Salas, Robert. 2015. *Unidentified: The UFO Phenomenon: How World Governments Have Conspire to Conceal Humanity's Biggest Secret.* New Page Books, Pompton Plains, NJ.

Schindele, David. D. 2017. *It Never Happened,*

Volume 1: U.S. Air Force UFO Cover-up Revealed. Edgarrock Publishing, Mukilteo, WA.

Simmel, Georg. "The Sociology of Secrecy and of Secret Societies." *American Journal of Sociology*

Swann, Ingo. 1998. *Penetration: The Question of Extraterrestrial and Human Telepathy.* Ingo Swann Books.

Taleb, Nassim Nicholas. 2012. *AntiFragile: Things That Gain from Disorder.* Random House, New York.

_____. 2010. *The Black Swan, Second Edition: The Impact of the Highly Improbable.* Random House, New York.

Tegmark, Max. 2014. *Our Mathematical Universe: My Quest for the Ulitmate Nature of Reality.* Alfred A. Knopf, NY.

Warren, Larry and Peter Robbins. 2015. *Left at East Gate: A First-Hand Account of the Bentwaters/-Woodbridge UFO Incident, Its Cover-up and Investigation.* Da Capo Press.

Weber, Max. 1978. *Economy and Society.* University of California Press, Berkeley.

Westrum, Ron. 1979. "Knowledge about Sea Serpents." in *On the Margins of Science: The Social Construction of Rejected Knowledge* edited by Roy Wallis. University of Keele.

Wiseman, Richard. *The As If Principle: The Radically New Approach to Changing Your Life.* Free Press, Simon and Schuster, New York.

Wootton, David. 2015. *The Invention of Science: A New History of the Scientific Revolution.* Harper Collins Publishers.

_____. 2007. *Bad Medicine: Doctors Doing Harm Since Hippocrates.* Oxford University Press.

Zerubavel, Eviatar. 2007. *The Elephant in the Room: Silence and Denial in Everyday Life.* Oxford University Press.

Zimmerman, Linda. 2014. *Hudson Valley UFOs: Startling Eyewitness Accounts from 1909 to the Present.* Eagle Press, NY

About the Author

Simeon Hein

Dr. Simeon Hein is the director of a research and teaching company, the Mount Baldy Institute, which he founded in 1997, to give people the opportunity to learn Virtual Viewing, a type of intuition training that taps into our creative unconscious intelligence.

He also studies crop circles and takes people on

crop circle tours. You can watch some of his lectures about crop circles. He is an avid acoustic guitarist: You can listen to his music here.

He has written a number of previous books including *Opening Minds: A Journey of Extraordinary Encounters, Crop Circles, and Resonance* and more recently, *Planetary Intelligence: 101 Easy Steps to Energy, Well Being, and Natural Insight.* You can find Simeon on YouTube and Twitter. Read his blog at NewCrystalMind.com.

Made in the USA
Coppell, TX
05 March 2022

74525012R00121